ZANER-BLOSER
Spell It—Write!

Karen R. Harris, Ed.D.   Steve Graham, Ed.D.   Jerry Zutell, Ph.D.

J. Richard Gentry, Ph.D.

Zaner-Bloser, Inc.
Columbus, Ohio

Contributing Author

Richard Lutz, Ph.D.
Adjunct Professor,
Applied Linguistics
Georgetown University
Washington, D.C.

Program Consultants

Delores Block
Language Arts Supervisor
Round Rock, Texas

Alan Cox, Ph.D.
Language Arts Supervisor
Fort Worth, Texas

A. John Dalmolin II
Elementary Principal
Phoenix, Arizona

Graciela Farias
Language Arts Supervisor
McAllen, Texas

Gladys Hillman-Jones
Educational Consultant
South Orange, New Jersey

Jean S. Mann
Educational Consultant
Sharon, New Hampshire

Robert McGrattan
Elementary Principal
Asheville, North Carolina

George Mundine
Elementary Principal
Houston, Texas

Fran Norris
Language Arts Director
Conroe, Texas

Patti Pace
Assistant Elementary Principal
Houston, Texas

Loretta Parker
School Services Consultant
Reading Specialist
Corpus Christi, Texas

Terry Ross
Language Arts Supervisor
Round Rock, Texas

Grade Level Consultants

María A. Alanis
Chapter I Coordinator
Austin, Texas

Ella Bell
Sixth Grade Teacher
Shenandoah Junction, West Virginia

Patricia Boyd
Seventh Grade Teacher
Cheektowaga, New York

Claudia Cornett, Ph.D.
Professor, Education
Wittenberg University
Springfield, Ohio

Deborah S. Daniels
Fifth Grade Teacher
Portsmouth, Virginia

Michele Gagen
Kindergarten Teacher
Columbus, Ohio

Marlene Goodman
Second Grade Teacher
St. John, Indiana

Dominic F. Gullo, Ph.D.
Professor, Early Childhood Education
University of Wisconsin–Milwaukee
Milwaukee, Wisconsin

Nancy Hamlet
Reading Specialist
Glendale, Arizona

Beverly Hill
Fourth Grade Teacher
Booneville, Mississippi

Janice T. Jones
Prekindergarten Facilitator
Chicago, Illinois

Denise Larson
Third Grade Teacher
Portland, Oregon

Debra M. Leatherwood
Third Grade Teacher
Candler, North Carolina

Cathy Maloney
Fifth Grade Teacher
Boise, Idaho

Peter Monether
Middle School Teacher
Fitzwilliam, New Hampshire

Cheryl Prescott
First Grade Teacher
Brandon, Florida

Anita Ross
Kindergarten Teacher
Detroit, Michigan

Janet Strong
Eighth Grade Teacher
West Point, Mississippi

Mary Thomas Vallens
Fourth Grade Teacher
Irvine, California

Spanish Language Consultants

Maria M. Corsino Bolander
Houston, Texas

Amalia Hernandez
San Antonio, Texas

Lucy Herrera
Weslaco, Texas

Joan Nieto
Columbus, Ohio

Sources for word histories and etymologies include:

Ayto, John. *Dictionary of Word Origins.* New York: Arcade Publishing, 1990.
Barnhart, Robert K., ed. *The Barnhart Dictionary of Etymology.* New York: The H.W. Wilson Company, 1988.
Claiborne, Robert. *The Roots of English.* New York: Anchor Books, Doubleday, 1989.

Spell It—Write! referred to *Webster's Ninth New Collegiate Dictionary* in the development of these materials. *Webster's Ninth New Collegiate Dictionary.* Springfield, MA: Merriam-Webster Inc., 1988.

Editorial and Production Development: Brown Publishing Network

Illustrations:

Cover: Theo Rudnak
Student Edition: Ellen Joy Sasaki
Game Mats: Ron Leiser

ISBN: 0-88085-385-9

Copyright © 1998 Zaner-Bloser, Inc.

Zaner-Bloser, Inc., P.O. Box 16764, Columbus, Ohio 43216-6764 (1-800-421-3018)

Printed in the United States of America   98 99 00 01 WC 5 4 3 2

TABLE OF CONTENTS

Welcome to *Spell It–Write!* It's a new and different spelling program. In *Spell It–Write!* you will learn important spelling patterns. You will also learn important spelling strategies.

4 Table of Contents

Did you know that learning to spell is a process? You'll learn to find words to make your spelling list. Then you'll inspect and master those words. This will help you develop good spelling habits.

Spelling Process Handbook

> **Word hunting** is simple—you hunt for words you need to know how to spell. You hunt words in your writing, words in your reading, and words that interest you. Good word hunters find words they use often but cannot spell.

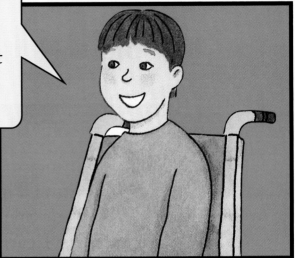

WORD Hunting

Ask yourself:

- "Do I already know how to spell this word?"
  If you can spell a word easily, hunt another word.
- "Do I know what this word means?"
  If a word catches your interest and you're not sure what it means, find the meaning first.

Collect the word.

Write the word in your list of **Words I Need to Know How to Spell**. Each week you will choose some of these words to learn to spell.

Check the spelling.

Check the spelling carefully when you write a word in **Words I Need to Know How to Spell**. If you copied the word from a sign or a book, compare how you wrote the word with how it is spelled on the sign or in the book. You might also use a dictionary or ask someone who knows the correct spelling.

WORD Hunting Tips

Your Writing

- Circle words you think you may have misspelled.

- Tape an index card to your desk. Write words you are not sure of on the card.

- Ask a partner to check your writing for spelling mistakes.

Your Reading

- Use a piece of paper as a bookmark. Write words you would like to learn how to spell on the bookmark.

- Write interesting words on self-sticking notes. Stick them to the edges of the pages in your book.

Other Words

- Carry a little notebook. Write words from signs and newspapers.

Save Your Words

- Remember to save words in your **Words I Need to Know How to Spell**.

Share Your Words

- Write words you have hunted on cards. Post them in your classroom.

- With a partner, talk about words you have hunted. Tell why you hunted each word. Ask about the words your partner has hunted.

Building Your Spelling List

Each week, you build your spelling list. These are the words you want to learn that week. Your spelling list will be made of three different kinds of words.

Pattern Words or Strategy Words

Every *Spell It–Write!* unit helps you understand an important spelling pattern or strategy. You will take a pretest on **Pattern Words** or **Strategy Words** each week.

Write words you misspell on the pretest on your spelling list.

Teacher Words

Your teacher may give you more words to learn how to spell. These could be other words that match the spelling pattern or strategy. They could also be words from other school work or words your teacher knows you have trouble spelling.

Write words from your teacher on your spelling list.

Your Words

Pick words from your list of **Words I Need to Know How to Spell**. These are words from your writing and your reading.

Write these words on your spelling list.

Make sure you spell all the words correctly when you write your spelling list.

Setting Your Learning Goal

Each week you set a learning goal to spell all the words on your spelling list. Try to learn at least ten words that you do not already know how to spell. Some weeks you may choose to set a higher goal.

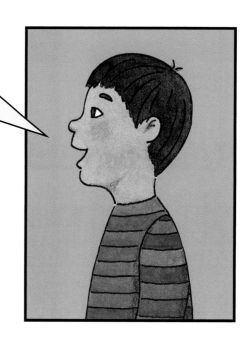

To set your goal:

Count your spelling words.

Count the number of words on your spelling list.

Write the number.

Write the number of words that is your goal. At the end of the unit, you will compare this number with the score on your spelling test.

Sorting WORDS

Sorting words is fun! It helps you learn how the **Spelling Pattern** or the **Spelling Strategy** works.

Sometimes you will sort spelling words. This will help you see how the words are alike—and how they are different!

You can sort words in lots of different ways.

• **Sort words by hearing how they sound**

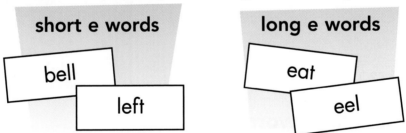

short e words

bell

left

long e words

eat

eel

• **Sort words by their spelling patterns**

long a spelled ay

may hay

pay

long a spelled ai

hail

pail

long a spelled a-consonant-e

tale

whale

• **Sort words by what they mean.**

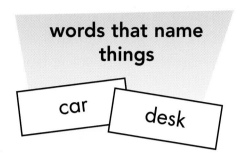

words that name things

car

desk

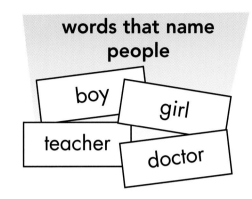

words that name people

boy

girl

teacher

doctor

No matter how you sort words, you may have a word that doesn't fit. You can put that word under a question mark.

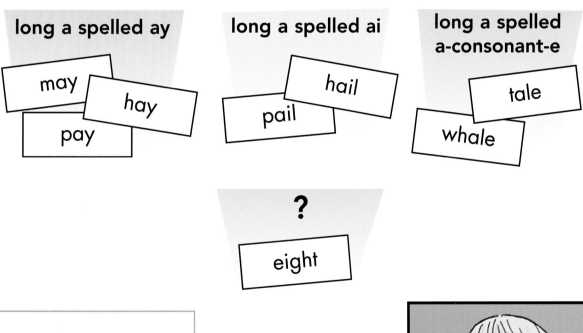

long a spelled ay

may

hay

pay

long a spelled ai

hail

pail

long a spelled a-consonant-e

tale

whale

?

eight

Ask your teacher about **Hands-on Word Sort Cards** and a **Hands-on Word Sort Sheet**. They are available for certain units.

What new ways can you think of to sort words?

Practicing Your Spelling List Independently

> Each week you get to choose activities to help you practice and learn your spelling words. These activities make your learning plan. Here are some tips on making your plan.

- **Pick more than one activity.**

  Spell It–Write! gives you lots of choices. Don't try to do everything on the plan every week. Pick at least three different activities that you enjoy.

- **Try every activity at least once.**

  You'll like some activities better than others. But at the start of the year, you should try every activity a few times to see how it works for you.

- **Stick with your learning plan.**

  Once you make your plan, stick with it. If your plan doesn't work well, you can make a new plan with different choices the next week.

> Read the next few pages to learn lots of fun practice activities. **Try them all!**

Game Mats

1. Find the game mat for the game you want in the *Spell It–Write!* classroom package.
2. Find a partner.
3. Use directions—and your spelling list—to play the game.

 Funny Faces

 Ski Race

 Spelling Road Race

 Spelling Snakes

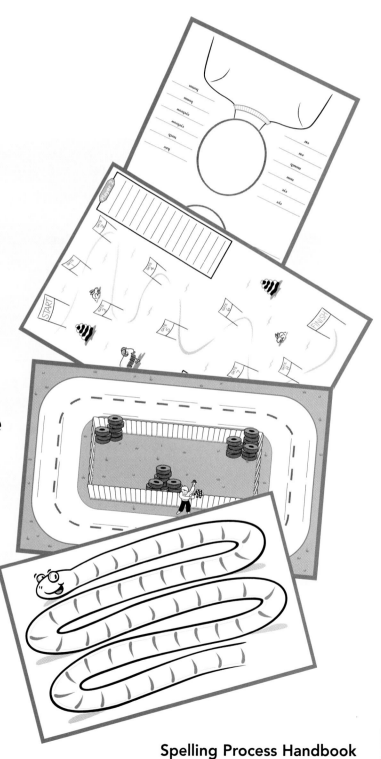

On Your Own

 Spelling Study Strategy

Look, Say, Cover, See, Write, Check, Rewrite

1. Look at the word you want to learn.

2. Say the word.

3. Cover the word. See the word in your mind. (You may want to close your eyes.)

4. Write the word.

5. Check your spelling.

6. Rewrite the word correctly.

You can use the **Spelling Study Strategy** and the **Flip Folder** to learn any spelling words!

Flip Folder

1. Get a **Flip Folder** and **Flip Folder** Practice Sheet.

2. Print your spelling list in the first column of your **Flip Folder** Practice Sheet. Make sure you spelled each word right.

3. Slide your Practice Sheet into the **Flip Folder**.

4. Open Flap 1.
  –Look at the first word.
  –Say the word.

5. Close Flap 1.
  –See the word in your mind. (You may want to close your eyes.)

6. Open Flap 2.
  –Write the word on the first line.

7. Open Flap 1 and Flap 2 at the same time.
  –Check your spelling.

8. Open Flap 3.
  –Write the word again.

9. Open Flaps 1 and 3 at the same time.
  –Check your spelling.

With a Partner

 ## Spelling Tic-Tac-Toe

1. Find a partner.

2. Trade spelling lists. Make sure you can read all the words on each other's lists.

3. Decide who will go first. (It's best to take turns going first.) Decide who will use **X** and who will use **O**.

4. Draw a tic-tac-toe board on a piece of scrap paper.

5. Say the first word on your partner's list out loud. Your partner should spell the word out loud while you use his list to check the spelling. If your partner is correct, he should write **X** or **O** (the one he's using) on the tic-tac-toe board. If your partner is not right, you should spell the word correctly—out loud and one letter at a time.

6. Trade jobs.

7. Keep taking turns until you or your partner makes three **X**'s or three **O**'s in a line on the board. If you fill up the board before either of you makes a line, start again.

At Home

Take Your Spelling List Home

Spell It–Write! has lots of fun ways to learn more about spelling at home. Word play can be fun for the whole family, so don't forget to do spelling activities at home, too.

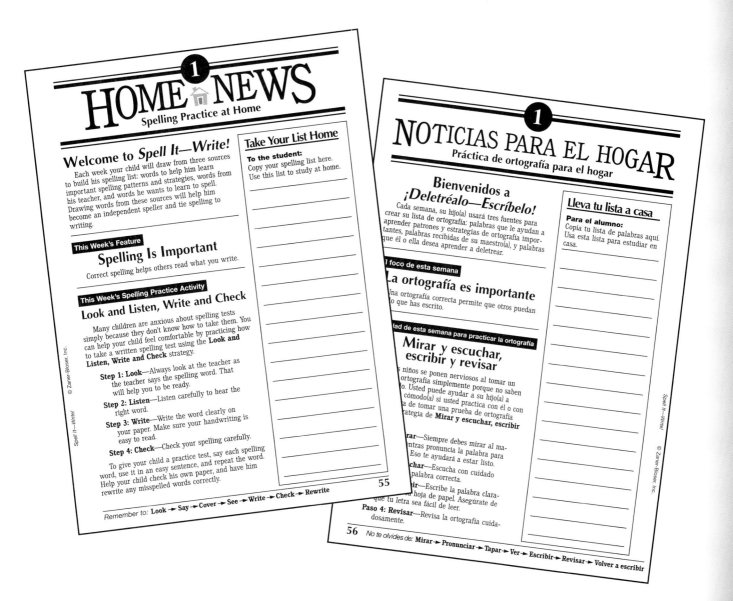

HOME NEWS
Spelling Practice at Home

Welcome to *Spell It—Write!*

Each week your child will draw from three sources to build his spelling list: words to help him learn important spelling patterns and strategies, words from his teacher, and words he wants to learn to spell. Drawing words from these sources will help him become an independent speller and tie spelling to writing.

This Week's Feature
Spelling Is Important

Correct spelling helps others read what you write.

This Week's Spelling Practice Activity
Look and Listen, Write and Check

Many children are anxious about spelling tests simply because they don't know how to take them. You can help your child feel comfortable by practicing how to take a written spelling test using the **Look and Listen, Write and Check** strategy.

Step 1: Look—Always look at the teacher as the teacher says the spelling word. That will help you to be ready.

Step 2: Listen—Listen carefully to hear the right word.

Step 3: Write—Write the word clearly on your paper. Make sure your handwriting is easy to read.

Step 4: Check—Check your spelling carefully.

To give your child a practice test, say each spelling word, use it in an easy sentence, and repeat the word. Help your child check his own paper, and have him rewrite any misspelled words correctly.

Remember to: **Look → Say → Cover → See → Write → Check → Rewrite**

Take Your List Home

To the student:
Copy your spelling list here. Use this list to study at home.

55

NOTICIAS PARA EL HOGAR
Práctica de ortografía para el hogar

Bienvenidos a ¡Deletréalo—Escríbelo!

Cada semana, su hijo(a) usará tres fuentes para crear su lista de ortografía: palabras que le ayudan a aprender patrones y estrategias de ortografía importantes, palabras recibidas de su maestro(a), y palabras que él o ella desea aprender a deletrear.

El foco de esta semana
La ortografía es importante

Una ortografía correcta permite que otros puedan leer lo que has escrito.

Actividad de esta semana para practicar la ortografía
Mirar y escuchar, escribir y revisar

Los niños se ponen nerviosos al tomar un examen de ortografía simplemente porque no saben cómo hacerlo. Usted puede ayudar a su hijo(a) a sentirse cómodo(a) si usted practica con él o con ella la manera de tomar una prueba de ortografía con la estrategia de **Mirar y escuchar, escribir y revisar**

Mirar—Siempre debes mirar al maestro mientras pronuncia la palabra para deletrear. Eso te ayudará a estar listo.

Escuchar—Escucha con cuidado para oír la palabra correcta.

Escribir—Escribe la palabra claramente en una hoja de papel. Asegúrate de que tu letra sea fácil de leer.

Paso 4: Revisar—Revisa la ortografía cuidadosamente.

No te olvides de: **Mirar → Pronunciar → Tapar → Ver → Escribir → Revisar → Volver a escribir**

56

Lleva tu lista a casa

Para el alumno:
Copia tu lista de palabras aquí. Usa esta lista para estudiar en casa.

© Zaner-Bloser, Inc.
Spell It—Write!

> **Developing good spelling habits** means knowing that correct spelling is important. Correct spelling makes it easier for others to read your writing. Correct spelling means that you care about your work!

Taking **Spelling Tests**

Taking a Self-Test

1. Look at the first word on your spelling list. Cover the word. Write the word.

2. Do this for each word on your list.

3. Use your spelling list to check your test.

4. Write the correct spelling next to any word you did not spell correctly.

Taking a Test (or a Practice Test) With a Partner

1. Find a partner. Give your partner your spelling list. Make sure your partner can read each word on your list.

2. Write your test in pencil. (Use a pen to correct your test.)

3. Ask your partner to read your words out loud, one at a time.

4. Listen carefully. Ask your partner to repeat any word you don't understand.

5. Write the words on a piece of paper.

6. Use your spelling list to correct your own test. Write the correct spelling next to any word you did not spell correctly.

Giving a Test to a Partner

1. Read your partner's spelling list to yourself before the test. If you don't know how to say a word, ask your partner or your teacher to help you.

2. Say each word clearly. Make sure your partner heard the word. Say it again if you need to.

3. Give your partner time to write that word. Say the next word.

Checking a Spelling Test Letter-by-Letter

1. Get out your pen, your spelling list, and your test.

2. Put the first word on the test paper next to the first word on the spelling list. Check the spelling one letter at a time. (You may want to point to each letter. You can say each letter in the correct spelling out loud, too.)

3. If the word is spelled wrong, circle it. Write the correct spelling next to the mistake.

4. Keep going until you have checked every word.

Graphing Your Progress

Color the number of words you spelled correctly on your spelling test at the end of the week. Use the graph in the back of your book or a graph from your teacher.

Saving Missed Words

Keep track of the words you misspelled on your unit tests. Write the words you misspelled in your list of **Words I Need to Know How to Spell**. Check the spelling to make sure you wrote each word correctly. Put these words on your spelling list again later.

SPELLING STRATEGY

1

Spelling Is Important

STEP 1

Build Your Spelling List

Find Your Strategy Words

Add Teacher Words

Add Your Words

Strategy Words

1. **wish** I **wish** the rain would stop.
2. **help** I'll **help** you lift the big box.
3. **went** Ann **went** to the park with Mom.
4. **down** My sled flew **down** the hill.
5. **wet** The dog shook its **wet** fur.
6. **zoo** We saw lions and tigers at the **zoo**.
7. **miss** Did you **miss** the bus?
8. **rest** Cindy ate the **rest** of the grapes.

STEP 2 ## Write Your Spelling List

STEP 3 ## Set Your Learning Goal

My spelling list has _____ words.

What a short word list! It only has eight words.

Yes, those are the **Strategy Words**. You add more words to build your own spelling list each week.

Explore the Spelling Strategy

Check It!

Read the signs below. Write the correct spelling of each underlined word. Use the list of **Strategy Words** on page 22 to check your spelling.

1. You'll have fun at the <u>zew</u>.
2. Your <u>wich</u> will come true at Fun Park!
3. Careful—<u>wett</u> paint!
4. Dial 911 for <u>hulp</u>.
5. One mile to <u>ress</u> stop.
6. Don't <u>mis</u> the big dog show!
7. Come on <u>dowen</u> to our shoe sale!
8. Don't know where your money <u>wehnt</u>? Use our bank!

1. _____

2. _____

3. _____

4. _____

5. _____

6. _____

7. _____

8. _____

Focus on Word Study

Be a Word Hunter!

It's fun to hunt and collect interesting words. Hunt in a piece of your writing for two words that you have misspelled or are not sure how to spell.

1. Write the words you find.

   _____   _____

   _____   _____

2. Check the spelling carefully.

3. Now copy the words under the first letter of each word in **Words I Need to Know How to Spell**.

Spelling Strategy
Correct spelling helps others read what you write.

STEP 6 Practice Your Spelling List Independently

Choose at least three activities to practice your spelling list.

Game Mats

○ Funny Faces   ○ Ski Race

With a Partner

○ Spelling Tic-Tac-Toe

On Your Own

○ Flip Folder   ○ Spelling Study Strategy

At Home

○ Take Your List Home

 Practice the Spelling Strategy

It's your turn to be the teacher! One word in each group is spelled right. Write the correct word.

Strategy Words

wish
help
went
down
wet
zoo
miss
rest

1. wet   wett   wat   _____

2. help   hlep   hilp   _____

3. wint   whent   went   _____

4. whish   wish   wich   _____

5. zu   zoo   zue   _____

6. down   doun   dowun   _____

7. resst   rest   rist   _____

8. miss   mis   micc   _____

STEP 7 Focus on Writing

A. Proofread the Writing of Others

Read the story Scott wrote. Find the four words that are spelled wrong. Write the correct spelling.

I wennt to the zu today. The man who

fed the seals let me halp him. I got all wit!

Make a capital.
Make a small letter.
Add something.
Take out something.
Add a period.
New paragraph
SP Spelling error

1. _____

2. _____

3. _____

4. _____

B. Proofread Your Own Writing

Proofread your latest piece of writing. If you find a word that is spelled wrong, draw a line through it. Write the correct spelling above it.

C. A Writing Idea: A Friendly Note

Where do you wish you could go? Would you like to go to the zoo? Write a note to a friend. Tell where you would like to go. Tell why you want to go there. Before you give the note to your friend, check to be sure all the words are spelled correctly.

STEP 8 Check Your Weekly Progress

▶ **Take the Test**

▶ **Check Your Goal**

▶ **Graph Your Progress**

▶ **Save Missed Words**
Write the words you missed in your list of **Words I Need to Know How to Spell**.

SPELLING PATTERN

2

**Short Vowels:
a, e, i**

1 Build Your Spelling List

Find Your Pattern Words

Add Teacher Words

Add Your Words

Pattern Words

1. **land**   We'll build a house on this **land**.

2. **men**   Six **men** ran in the race.

3. **fix**   I can **fix** my own lunch.

4. **king**   The **king** sits on a gold chair.

5. **grass**   Mom cut the **grass** this morning.

6. **next**   My grandma will visit us **next** week.

7. **bat**   Bobby hit the ball with his lucky **bat**.

8. **inch**   This bug is one **inch** long.

STEP 2 Write Your Spelling List

STEP 3 Set Your Learning Goal

My spelling list has _____ words.

> I write all the **Pattern Words** in my spelling list.

> I only put down the words I miss in my pretest. I can add other words to my list, too.

Explore the Spelling Pattern
Sorting Words

Sort the **Pattern Words** into three groups. Use the vowel sound in each word below to guide your sort. Make sure you write each **Pattern Word** once.

Try sorting the **Pattern Words** in other ways. Can you put the words in A–B–C order?

1. l̲and

2. fi̲x

3. me̲n

Focus on Word Study
More Than One Meaning

Some words have more than one meaning. You know that a **bat** is a stick you use to hit a ball. Did you know there is a flying animal that is called a **bat**?

Write the short vowel word that matches each pair of meanings.

1. a machine that blows air

   a person who loves sports

2. something you sleep on

   a place where flowers grow

▼▼▼▼▼▼▼▼▼▼▼▼▼
Spelling Pattern

- Listen to the vowel sound in **land**. It is called **short a** and is spelled with an **a**.

- Listen to the vowel sound in **men**. It is called **short e** and is spelled with an **e**.

- Listen to the vowel sound in **fix**. It is called **short i** and is spelled with an **i**.

STEP 6 Practice Your Spelling List Independently

Choose at least three activities to practice your spelling list.

Game Mats

○ Ski Race   ○ Spelling Road Race

With a Partner

○ Spelling Tic-Tac-Toe

On Your Own

○ Flip Folder   ○ Spelling Study Strategy

At Home

○ Take Your List Home

Practice the Spelling Pattern

Write the **Pattern Word** that fits each sentence.
Then circle the vowel in each word you wrote.

Pattern Words

land
men
fix
king
grass
next
bat
inch

1. In spring, the __ grows tall.

2. May I sit __ to you?

3. We have a president, not a __.

4. A __ eats lots of bugs.

5. Two __ painted our house.

6. One __ is not very big.

7. The plane flew above the __.

8. A woman came to __ our TV.

STEP 7 Focus on  Writing

A. Proofread the Writing of Others

Decide which type of mistake, if any, appears in each underlined part of this story.

The Big Game

The home team was <u>up at batt.</u> "Don't give
①
<u>an insh!"</u> someone yelled. Crack! Where would
②
the ball <u>land It</u> went over the fence and into the
③
<u>grass. our</u> team won!
④

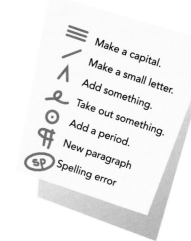

Make a capital.
Make a small letter.
Add something.
Take out something.
Add a period.
New paragraph
SP Spelling error

1. **A** Spelling
   B Capitalization
   C Punctuation
   D No mistake

2. **A** Spelling
   B Capitalization
   C Punctuation
   D No mistake

3. **A** Spelling
   B Capitalization
   C Punctuation
   D No mistake

4. **A** Spelling
   B Capitalization
   C Punctuation
   D No mistake

B. Proofread Your Own Writing

Look for **short a, short e,** and **short i** words in your writing. Correct misspelled words. Write them in **Words I Need to Know How to Spell.**

C. A Writing Idea: A Story

Use **Pattern Words** to make up story titles. Write a story to go with the title you like best.

STEP 8 Check Your Weekly Progress

▶ **Take the Test**

▶ **Check Your Goal**

▶ **Graph Your Progress**

▶ **Save Missed Words**
Write the words you missed in your list of **Words I Need to Know How to Spell.**

SPELLING PATTERN

3

**Short Vowels:
o, u**

STEP 1 Build Your Spelling List

Find Your Pattern Words

Add Teacher Words

Add Your Words

Pattern Words

1. **fox**   The **fox** has a bushy tail.
2. **bus**   I ride a **bus** to school.
3. **lot**   We saw a **lot** of clowns at the circus.
4. **jump**   My dog can **jump** over a fence.
5. **doll**   Molly made a green dress for her **doll**.
6. **cut**   Kevin **cut** a circle from the yellow paper.
7. **drop**   A **drop** of rain fell on my nose.
8. **cup**   The **cup** is full of milk.

STEP 2 Write Your Spelling List

STEP 3 Set Your Learning Goal

My spelling list has _____ words.

Will our teacher give us more **Pattern Words**?

Yes, I think she'll give us a few science words, too. That will help us write about science.

Explore the Spelling Pattern
Sorting Words

Sort the **Pattern Words** into two groups. Use the vowels in the words below to guide your sort. Make sure you write each **Pattern Word** once.

1. f o x

2. b u s

Try sorting the **Pattern Words** in other ways. Which words are spelled with only three letters?

▼ ▼ ▼ ▼ ▼ ▼ ▼ ▼ ▼ ▼ ▼ ▼ ▼ ▼ ▼ ▼

Spelling Pattern

- Listen to the vowel sound in **fox**. It is called **short o** and is spelled with an **o**.

- Listen to the vowel sound in **bus**. It is called **short u** and is spelled with a **u**.

Focus on Word Study
Clipped Words

People can ride a bus to get where they need to go. Our word **bus** is short for a much older word, **omnibus**. **Omnibus** meant "wagon for everyone."

Write the short form for each of these words:

1. chimpanzee _____

2. bicycle _____

3. submarine _____

4. mathematics _____

STEP 6 Practice Your Spelling List Independently

Choose at least three activities to practice your spelling list.

Game Mats	With a Partner	On Your Own	At Home
○ Spelling Road Race ○ Spelling Snakes	○ Spelling Tic-Tac-Toe	○ Flip Folder ○ Spelling Study Strategy	○ Take Your List Home

Practice the Spelling Pattern

Use two **Pattern Words** with the same short vowel sound to finish each sentence. Then read the sentences aloud to be sure they make sense.

Pattern Words

fox
bus
lot
jump
doll
cut
drop
cup

1–2. We had to __ on the __ fast!

_____   _____
_____   _____
_____   _____

3–4. Don't __ yourself on the broken __.

_____   _____
_____   _____
_____   _____

5–6. Be careful not to __ the pretty __.

_____   _____
_____   _____
_____   _____

7–8. The mother __ had a __ of cubs.

_____   _____
_____   _____
_____   _____

STEP 7 Focus on Writing

A. Hunt Spelling Words in Your Writing

Choose one piece of your latest writing. Work with a spelling partner to look for **short o** words and **short u** words. Use two columns like these to write the words you found.

Make a capital.
Make a small letter.
Add something.
Take out something.
Add a period.
New paragraph
SP Spelling error

Column 1	Column 2
I spelled these **short o** and **short u** words correctly.	I misspelled these **short o** and **short u** words.

If you can't find any **short o** or **short u** words, choose a different piece of your writing.

Add the words you wrote in Column 2 to **Words I Need to Know How to Spell**.

B. A Writing Idea: A Paragraph

Do you go places by bus? By car? Have you ever gone on a plane? Write a paragraph about your favorite way to travel. Tell why it is your favorite.

STEP 8 Check Your Weekly Progress

▶ **Take the Test**

▶ **Check Your Goal**

▶ **Graph Your Progress**

▶ **Save Missed Words**
Write the words you missed in your list of **Words I Need to Know How to Spell**.

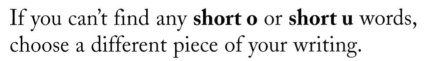

SPELLING STRATEGY 4

Use Rhyming Words

STEP 1 Build Your Spelling List

Find Your Strategy Words

Add Teacher Words

Add Your Words

Strategy Words

1. **hold** I'll **hold** your skates for you.
2. **tell** Shall I **tell** you a story?
3. **best** We like the outdoor games **best**.
4. **fold** Please **fold** your paper down the middle.
5. **keep** Can you **keep** a secret?
6. **call** Kiki will **call** you about the party.
7. **hill** We ran to the top of the **hill**.
8. **gold** My grandfather wears a **gold** ring.

STEP 2 Write Your Spelling List

STEP 3 Set Your Learning Goal

My spelling list has _____ words.

I wrote the words I missed on last week's test in **Words I Need to Know How to Spell**. I'll add them to my spelling list.

I didn't miss any words last week. I'll look for more **Strategy Words** in **More Words for Hungry Word Hunters**.

Explore the Spelling Strategy

Rhyme Time

The words in each group rhyme. The rhyming part of the words is spelled the same. Write a **Strategy Word** that rhymes with each word group.

1. ball   tall   fall   _____

2. sell   well   bell   _____

3. cold   told   sold   _____

4. rest   test   west   _____

5. bill   will   chill   _____

6. peep   deep   weep   _____

Focus on Word Study

Idioms

Some words are used in a lot of sayings. People say "Hold your horses!" when they want someone to slow down.

Write a word to complete each saying.

1. as good as __ (best, gold)   _____

2. __ it a day. (Call, Fold)   _____

▼▼▼▼▼▼▼▼▼▼▼▼▼▼▼

Spelling Strategy

If you're not sure how to spell a word, think of a word that rhymes. The last parts of rhyming words are often spelled the same.

▪▪▪▪▪▪▪▪▪▪▪▪▪▪▪

STEP 6 Practice Your Spelling List Independently

Choose at least three activities to practice your spelling list.

Game Mats	With a Partner	On Your Own	At Home

○ Funny
Faces

○ Spelling
Snakes

○ Spelling
Tic-Tac-Toe

○ Flip
Folder

○ Spelling
Study
Strategy

○ Take Your
List Home

 Practice the Spelling Strategy

Each underlined word rhymes with a **Strategy Word**. Write the rhyming **Strategy Word**.

Strategy Words

hold

tell

best

fold

keep

call

hill

gold

1. Please __ me when you hear the <u>bell</u>.

2. There may be __ in that <u>old</u> cave.

3. Will you help me __ this <u>old</u> blanket?

4. The farmer wants to __ the <u>sheep</u>.

5. This is the __ grade I ever got on a <u>test</u>.

6. You can __ your mother from the <u>mall</u>.

7. Jack and <u>Jill</u> went up the __.

8. Dad <u>told</u> me to __ my sister's hand.

STEP 7 Focus on Writing

A. Proofread the Writing of Others

Proofread this paragraph. Decide which type of mistake, if any, appears in each underlined part.

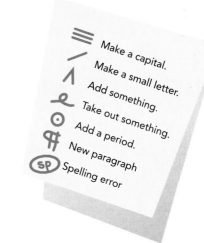

Make a capital.
Make a small letter.
Add something.
Take out something.
Add a period.
New paragraph
SP Spelling error

  <u>many people like</u> gold. They think gold
  ①
is the <u>besst</u> metal. If you dig <u>in a hil, you</u>
     ②   ③
might find gold. But don't tell anyone

<u>where you found it!</u>
         ④

1. A Spelling
    B Capitalization
    C Punctuation
    D No mistake

2. A Spelling
    B Capitalization
    C Punctuation
    D No mistake

3. A Spelling
    B Capitalization
    C Punctuation
    D No mistake

4. A Spelling
    B Capitalization
    C Punctuation
    D No mistake

B. Proofread Your Own Writing

Look for words you are not sure you have spelled right. For each word, think of a rhyming word you know how to spell.

C. A Writing Idea: A Poem

Write a rhyming poem. You might want to write about something you like best. Is it a bird in a nest? Is it taking a rest? Share your poem.

STEP 8 Check Your Weekly Progress

▶ **Take the Test**

▶ **Check Your Goal**

▶ **Graph Your Progress**

▶ **Save Missed Words**
Write the words you missed in your list of **Words I Need to Know How to Spell**.

SPELLING PATTERN

5

Short a: a
Long a: a-C-e

STEP 1 Build Your Spelling List

> Find Your Pattern Words

> Add Teacher Words

> Add Your Words

Pattern Words

1. **mad**   My grandma almost never gets **mad**.
2. **made**   Look at the mask I **made**!
3. **have**   Do you **have** a blue crayon?
4. **bath**   The **bath** water is too hot!
5. **grade**   We are in second **grade**.
6. **hand**   Derek writes with his left **hand**.
7. **take**   Dad will **take** the baby to the park.
8. **add**   I can **add** big numbers.
9. **game**   Our **game** begins at two o'clock.
10. **ask**   **Ask** the teacher to help us.
11. **gave**   Mrs. Miller **gave** me this book.
12. **ate**   We **ate** lunch outside today.

STEP 2 Write Your Spelling List

STEP 3 Set Your Learning Goal

My spelling list has _____ words.

> I do, too! And I write words I misspelled in my writing. I also add any fun words I find.

> I write the words I spelled wrong on our spelling test in **Words I Need to Know How to Spell**.

STEP

4 Explore the Spelling Pattern

Sorting Words

Find a partner. Take turns reading the **Pattern Words** out loud. Sort the words into three groups. Use the words below to guide your sort. If a word doesn't fit, put it with the question mark.

You may wish to use **Hands-on Word Sort Cards** and the **Hands-on Word Sort Sheet** for this unit.

1. mad

2. made

3. ?

▼▼▼▼▼▼▼▼▼▼▼▼▼▼▼

Spelling Pattern

- Listen to **mad**. The **short a** sound is spelled **a**.

- Listen to **made**. The **long a** sound is spelled **a-consonant-silent e**.

STEP

5 Focus on Word Study

Place Names

Many words come from the name of a place. Write the ordinary word that came from the place suggested by each clue.

1. Dad cooked (meat patties named for a city in Germany) on the grill.

2. I made a peanut butter and jelly (place in England).

STEP 6 Practice Your Spelling List Independently

Choose at least three activities to practice your spelling list.

Game Mats

○ Funny Faces

○ Ski Race

With a Partner

○ Spelling Tic-Tac-Toe

On Your Own

○ Flip Folder

○ Spelling Study Strategy

At Home

○ Take Your List Home

Practice the Spelling Pattern

Write the **Pattern Word** that matches each tongue twister. You'll only use eight words.

Pattern Words

mad
made
have
bath
grade
hand
take
add
game
ask
gave
ate

1. Amy __ all the apples.

2. Baby birds had a __ in the birdbath.

3. Maude made Milly __.

4. Giddy goats galloped in a __.

5. Hank's __ held a hairy hamster.

6. Mom __ Mark many mittens.

7. Gail __ Glen a great gift!

8. __ ten turns to tap ten times.

STEP 7 Focus on Writing

A. Proofread the Writing of Others

Check the beginning of Rita's how-to for a card game. Find the four words that are not spelled right. Write each word correctly.

Make a capital.
Make a small letter.
Add something.
Take out something.
Add a period.
New paragraph
SP Spelling error

First, taik five cards. Do you hav any

pairs? If not, aks someone for a card. If you

maid a pair, put it down!

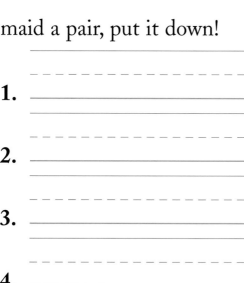

1. _____

2. _____

3. _____

4. _____

B. Proofread Your Own Writing

Look in your latest piece of writing for words with **short a** and **long a** vowel sounds. Check to be sure you have used the correct spellings. Correct any misspelled words. Write them in **Words I Need to Know How to Spell**.

C. A Writing Idea: A How-to

Work with a partner. Think of a game you both know how to play. Write a list of steps that tell how to play the game. Be sure to write the steps in the correct order.

STEP 8 Check Your Weekly Progress

▶ **Take the Test**

▶ **Check Your Goal**

▶ **Graph Your Progress**

▶ **Save Missed Words**
Write the words you missed in your list of **Words I Need to Know How to Spell**.

SPELLING PATTERN

6

Long a

STEP 1 Build Your Spelling List

Find Your Pattern Words

Add Teacher Words

Add Your Words

Pattern Words

1.	**base**	John slid into second **base**.
2.	**nail**	I hung the picture on the **nail**.
3.	**lay**	**Lay** the wet paintings on the table.
4.	**baby**	Mrs. Lopez has a new **baby**.
5.	**cake**	What kind of **cake** do you like?
6.	**away**	Please put the games **away**.
7.	**late**	Hurry, or we'll be **late**!
8.	**pay**	How much did you **pay** for lunch?
9.	**rain**	The **rain** sounds like music.
10.	**today**	Do we have art class **today**?
11.	**paid**	Mr. Yi **paid** me to walk his dog.
12.	**way**	Which **way** should I go?

STEP 2 Write Your Spelling List

STEP 3 Set Your Learning Goal

My spelling list has _____ words.

I really like doing fun activities to learn my words!

I like practicing my spelling words different ways. I work by myself or with a partner.

STEP 4

Explore the Spelling Pattern
Sorting Words

Find a partner. Take turns reading the **Pattern Words** out loud. Sort the **Pattern Words** into four groups. Use the words below to guide your sort. If a word doesn't fit, put it with the question mark. Write each **Pattern Word** once.

You may wish to use **Hands-on Word Sort Cards** and the **Hands-on Word Sort Sheet** for this unit.

1. l<u>ay</u>   **2. n<u>ai</u>l**   **3. b<u>a</u>s<u>e</u>**   **4. ?**

STEP 5

Focus on Word Study
Word Families

Words are in the same family if they are spelled alike. **Lay** and **pay** are in the **-ay** family.

Read the meanings. Write the **Pattern Word** in the **-ay** family that matches each meaning.

1. this day

2. from a place

Spelling Pattern

• Listen to **base**. The **long a** sound in this word is spelled **a-consonant-silent e**.

• Listen to **nail**. The **long a** sound is spelled **ai**.

• Listen to **lay**. The **long a** sound is spelled **ay**.

STEP 6 Practice Your Spelling List Independently

Choose at least three activities to practice your spelling list.

Game Mats	With a Partner	On Your Own	At Home

○ Ski Race ○ Spelling Road Race   ○ Spelling Tic-Tac-Toe   ○ Flip Folder ○ Spelling Study Strategy   ○ Take Your List Home

Practice the Spelling Pattern

The eight **Pattern Words** in these sentences are missing letters. Write the word that fits each sentence.

Pattern Words

base
nail
lay
baby
cake
away
late
pay
rain
today
paid
way

1. Don't be l__ for school. _____

2. To__ was very hot. _____

3. Hit the n__, not your finger! _____

4. Would you like some c__? _____

5. What a cute b__! _____

6. The map shows which w__ to go. _____

7. The runner must touch the b__. _____

8. I get p__ to mow the lawn. _____

STEP 7 Focus on Writing

A. Proofread the Writing of Others

Find the four words that are not spelled right in Lee's poem. Write the correct spelling.

Mom says, "Get up!

Todaye is the day.   1. _____

This is the day

we're going awai!"   2. _____

I look out the window

and see the rane.   3. _____

I hope we won't be

lait for the train!   4. _____

Make a capital.
Make a small letter.
Add something.
Take out something.
Add a period.
New paragraph
SP Spelling error

STEP 8

Check Your Weekly Progress

▶ **Take the Test**

▶ **Check Your Goal**

▶ **Graph Your Progress**

▶ **Save Missed Words**
Write the words you missed in your list of **Words I Need to Know How to Spell**.

B. Proofread Your Own Writing

Find **long a** words in your latest piece of writing. Have you used the correct spelling?

C. A Writing Idea: A Weather Report

Did it rain today? What was the weather like? Write a weather report. Tell what the weather was like today. Check your spelling.

SPELLING PATTERN

SPELLING PATTERN

7

**Short e: e
Long e: ee**

STEP 1

Build Your Spelling List

Find Your Pattern Words

Add Teacher Words

Add Your Words

Pattern Words

1. **met**   I **met** Marta at the swimming pool.
2. **seen**   Have you **seen** my coat?
3. **end**   How does the story **end**?
4. **tree**   The apple **tree** has pretty flowers.
5. **egg**   There is a crack in this **egg**.
6. **seem**   Mike does not **seem** happy today.
7. **when**   **When** does summer begin?
8. **sleep**   Where do ducks **sleep**?

STEP 2

Write Your Spelling List

STEP 3

Set Your Learning Goal

My spelling list has _____ words.

Aren't the practice activities fun?

They sure are. And I can always look in my **Spelling Process Handbook** if I forget any directions.

STEP 4

Explore the Spelling Pattern
Sorting Words

Sort the **Pattern Words** into two groups. Use the words below to guide your sort. Make sure you write each **Pattern Word** once.

Try sorting the **Pattern Words** in other ways. Which words have more than two consonants?

1. m<u>e</u>t

2. s<u>ee</u>n

_____

_____

_____

_____

_____

_____

_____

_____

_____

_____

_____

_____

STEP 5

Focus on Word Study
Word History

The meanings of words can change over time. The word **egg** comes from an old word that means "bird."

1. Choose the **Pattern Word** that came from a word that meant "oak." (sleep, tree)

    _____

2. Which **Pattern Word** once meant "tired"? (sleep, tree)

    _____

▼▼▼▼▼▼▼▼▼▼▼▼▼▼▼▼

Spelling Pattern

• Listen to **met**. The **short e** sound is spelled **e**.

• Listen to **seen**. The **long e** sound is spelled **ee**.

■ ■ ■ ■ ■ ■ ■ ■ ■ ■ ■ ■ ■

STEP 6 Practice Your Spelling List Independently

Choose at least three activities to practice your spelling list.

Game Mats	With a Partner	On Your Own	At Home

○ Spelling Snakes   ○ Spelling Road Race   ○ Spelling Tic-Tac-Toe   ○ Flip Folder   ○ Spelling Study Strategy   ○ Take Your List Home

Practice the Spelling Pattern

Write the **Pattern Word** that fits each sentence.
Circle letters that spell the **long e** sound.

Pattern Words

met
seen
end
tree
egg
seem
when
sleep

1. How would you like me to cook your __?

2. __ is your birthday?

3. Carla and Sam __ last year.

4. The last person is at the __ of the line.

5. Have you ever __ a rainbow before?

6. There is a big pine __ in our yard.

7. The children __ happy playing the game.

8. Do you __ eight hours every night?

STEP 7 Focus on Writing

A. Hunt Spelling Words in Your Writing

Choose several pieces of your latest writing. Work with a spelling partner to look for words with the **short e** vowel sound spelled **e** and the **long e** vowel sound spelled **ee**. Use two columns like these to write the words you find.

Make a capital.
Make a small letter.
Add something.
Take out something.
Add a period.
New paragraph
SP Spelling error

Column 1	Column 2
I spelled these **short e** and **long e** words correctly.	I misspelled these **short e** and **long e** words.

Add the words you wrote in Column 2 to **Words I Need to Know How to Spell**.

B. A Writing Idea: A Paragraph

With a partner, make a list of words that tell about trees. Then use the words to write a paragraph about trees. When you are done, check to be sure you have spelled all the words right.

STEP 8 Check Your Weekly Progress

▶ **Take the Test**

▶ **Check Your Goal**

▶ **Graph Your Progress**

▶ **Save Missed Words**
Write the words you missed in your list of **Words I Need to Know How to Spell**.

SPELLING PATTERN

8

Long e

STEP 1

Build Your Spelling List

Find Your Pattern Words

Add Teacher Words

Add Your Words

Pattern Words

1. **need**   Does David **need** a new pencil?
2. **clean**   We will **clean** our desks today.
3. **happy**   I was **happy** when we won the game.
4. **any**   Robby does not have **any** clay.
5. **cheek**   Ann has blue paint on her **cheek**.
6. **read**   Ms. West likes to **read** stories to us.
7. **sheet**   I have one **sheet** of paper left.
8. **eat**   We **eat** lunch at noon.

STEP 2

Write Your Spelling List

STEP 3

Set Your Learning Goal

My spelling list has _____ words.

I like spelling. Maybe I should add more words to my list.

I really have to practice my words to get them all right! I'll stick with the number of words I have.

STEP 4 Explore the Spelling Pattern
Sorting Words

Try sorting the **Pattern Words** in other ways. How many words begin with a vowel?

Sort the **Pattern Words**. Use the vowel spelling patterns in the words below to guide your sort. Write each **Pattern Word** once.

1. n__eed__

2. cl__ean__

3. happ__y__

STEP 5 Focus on Word Study
Changes in Meaning

We get the word **happy** from the old word **hap**. A hap was luck or a chance for something good to happen. Now when we say we are happy, we mean we are glad, cheerful, or having fun.

Match the words **glad, cheer,** and **fun** with the old words they came from.

1. glæd _____

2. fon _____

3. chere _____

Spelling Pattern

• Listen to **need**. The **long e** sound in this word is spelled **ee**.

• Listen to **clean**. The **long e** sound is spelled **ea**.

• Listen to **happy**. The **long e** sound is spelled **y**.

6 Practice Your Spelling List Independently

Choose at least three activities to practice your spelling list.

Game Mats	**With a Partner**	**On Your Own**	**At Home**

○ Funny Faces   ○ Spelling Snakes   ○ Spelling Tic-Tac-Toe   ○ Flip Folder   ○ Spelling Study Strategy   ○ Take Your List Home

Practice the Spelling Pattern

Write the **Pattern Word** that answers each riddle.

Pattern Words

need
clean
happy
any
cheek
read
sheet
eat

1. With me you're very nice and neat,
   So wash your hands before you eat.

2. End my spelling with a **d**.
   I have two **e**'s. Can you find me?

3. I'm the soft part of your face.
   I get red when you run a race.

4. I'm a cover on your bed.
   You pull me over your head.

5. My **long e** sound is spelled with **y**.
   If you feel like this, you won't cry!

6. I'm what you do with a book.
   Check one out and take a look.

7. I rhyme with **penny**,
   But I look like **many**.

8. My **long e** sound is spelled **ea**.
   You do this three times a day.

STEP 7 Focus on Writing

A. Proofread the Writing of Others

Ana's mother left her a note. Check it for spelling. Find the four words that are not spelled right. Write the correct spellings.

Make a capital.
Make a small letter.
Add something.
Take out something.
Add a period.
New paragraph
SP Spelling error

Dear Ana,

Reed this before you go out to play. I nede your help. Please cleane off the table. Aunt Nita is coming to dinner. She will be happe to see you.

Love,
Mom

1. _____   3. _____

2. _____   4. _____

B. Proofread Your Own Writing

The **long e** sound may be spelled **ee, ea,** and **y.** Find your latest piece of writing. Look for **long e** words. Add misspelled words to **Words I Need to Know How to Spell**.

C. A Writing Idea: A Picture Caption

Draw a picture of something that makes you feel happy. Then write a few sentences that tell why this makes you happy. Check your spelling.

STEP 8 Check Your Weekly Progress

▶ **Take the Test**

▶ **Check Your Goal**

▶ **Graph Your Progress**

▶ **Save Missed Words**
Write the words you missed in your list of **Words I Need to Know How to Spell**.

Check **Your**

✓ Check Your Spelling

Review Test

Here is a fun way to review your progress on spelling patterns. First, take the review test your teacher will give you. Then, check your test.

1
2
3
4
5
6
7
8

9
10
11
12

Progress

Which words did you spell correctly? Use the **Spelling Pattern Mastery Chart** to find your mastery level for each spelling pattern.

Spelling Pattern Mastery Chart

Pattern	All Correct	None Correct
Short Vowels: a, e, i 1 5		
Short Vowels: o, u 7 9		
Short a, Long a 3 11		
Long a 8 10		
Short e, Long e 4 12		
Long e 2 6		

All Correct: Pattern Mastered
None Correct: Keep Working on the Pattern

✓ Check Your Writing

Work with a partner to check your writing for words that match each pattern. Write misspelled words in your **Words I Need to Know How to Spell**.

SPELLING STRATEGY

9

Using a Dictionary

1 Build Your Spelling List

Find Your Strategy Words

Add Teacher Words

Add Your Words

Strategy Words

1. **store**   Dad went to the **store** to buy milk.
2. **been**   We have **been** playing all day.
3. **more**   Do you need **more** paint for the picture?
4. **buy**   I will **buy** a toy for Suzy at the store.
5. **your**   Is this **your** lunch box?
6. **wind**   The **wind** blew away Tanya's hat.
7. **were**   We **were** at the baseball game.
8. **fall**   The leaves change color in the **fall**.

STEP

2 Write Your Spelling List

STEP

3 Set Your Learning Goal

My spelling list has _____ words.

Well, it depends on whether the teacher adds more words.

I study the same number of words each week. How about you?

STEP 4 Explore the Spelling Strategy
Looking Up Words

You can check spelling in a dictionary. You use A-B-C order to look up a word. In what part of a dictionary would you find each **Strategy Word**?

1. In the Beginning (a, b, c, d, e, f, g, h)	2. In the Middle (i, j, k, l, m, n, o, p)	3. In the End (q, r, s, t, u, v, w, x, y, z)

STEP 5 Focus on Word Study
Changes in Meaning

Over time, some words change meanings. The first meaning of **store** was "a good supply." Later, it meant "to put away." The newest meaning is "a place to buy things."

Match **fall** or **foot** to each pair of meanings.

1. to go down suddenly
    time of year when leaves drop from trees

2. part of your body at the end of your leg
    12 inches

▼ ▼ ▼ ▼ ▼ ▼ ▼ ▼ ▼ ▼ ▼ ▼

Spelling Strategy
A dictionary can help you spell words. Words in a dictionary are arranged in A-B-C order.

STEP 6 Practice Your Spelling List Independently

Choose at least three activities to practice your spelling list.

Game Mats

○ Funny Faces   ○ Ski Race

With a Partner

○ Spelling Tic-Tac-Toe

On Your Own

○ Flip Folder   ○ Spelling Study Strategy

At Home

○ Take Your List Home

Practice the Spelling Strategy

This is Tina's spelling dictionary. Help Tina add words to her dictionary in A-B-C order. Write the **Strategy Word** that belongs in each space.

Strategy Words

store
been
more
buy
your
wind
were
fall

add
bat
_____
1. _____
bus
_____
2. _____
cup
doll
egg
_____
3. _____

grass
hill
inch
jump
keep
land
_____
4. _____
need
paid
rain

_____
5. _____
tell
very
_____
6. _____
_____
7. _____
_____
8. _____
zoo

STEP 7 Focus on Writing

A. Proofread the Writing of Others

Proofread the journal writing below. Find four words that are spelled wrong. Write the correct spellings.

October 4

    I think fal is the best time of the year.

The whin blew hard today. There wer

leaves all over our yard. I helped Dad rake

them. Then mor leaves fell!

1. _____   3. _____

2. _____   4. _____

B. Proofread Your Own Writing

Proofread something you have written. Look for words you spelled wrong. Write them correctly in **Words I Need to Know How to Spell**.

C. A Writing Idea: A List

Work with a partner to think of things you can find out from a dictionary. Write a list of the things you think of. When your list is done, write a title for it.

STEP 8 Check Your Weekly Progress

▶ **Take the Test**

▶ **Check Your Goal**

▶ **Graph Your Progress**

▶ **Save Missed Words**
Write the words you missed in your list of **Words I Need to Know How to Spell**.

SPELLING PATTERN

10

**Short i,
Long i**

STEP 1 Build Your Spelling List

Find Your Pattern Words

Add Teacher Words

Add Your Words

Pattern Words

1. **bit**   The puppy **bit** my finger.
2. **bite**   Sam took a big **bite** of the apple.
3. **nice**   I like **nice** Mr. Jackson.
4. **hid**   We **hid** to surprise her.
5. **mile**   Rita lives one **mile** from school.
6. **line**   Linda is the first one in the **line**.
7. **hide**   I'll **hide** behind the chair.
8. **five**   My cat is **five** years old.

STEP 2 Write Your Spelling List

STEP 3 Set Your Learning Goal

My spelling list has _____ words.

I look in my **Words I Need to Know How to Spell** to find other words that match each week's pattern.

Hey, I like that idea!

STEP 4 Explore the Spelling Pattern

Sorting Words

Try sorting the **Pattern Words** in other ways. Which words start with **h**?

Sort the **Pattern Words** into two groups—words with the **long i** sound and words with the **short i** sound. Use the words below to guide your sort. Write each **Pattern Word** once.

1. b<u>i</u>t

2. b<u>i</u>t<u>e</u>

STEP 5 Focus on Word Study

More Than One Meaning

Adding one letter to a word can change the meaning and the way we say the word. **Hid** is an action, but a **hide** can be an animal's skin.

Choose a word to match each meaning. Then add **e** and write a new word.

1. I can wear a (tub, cap) and a __.

2. (Tap, Cap) the stick and __ the map to the wall.

▼▼▼▼▼▼▼▼▼▼▼▼▼▼
Spelling Pattern

• Listen to **bit**. The **short i** sound is spelled **i**.

• Listen to **bite**. The **long i** sound is spelled **i**-consonant-**silent e**.

STEP 6 Practice Your Spelling List Independently

Choose at least three activities to practice your spelling list.

Game Mats

○ Ski Race   ○ Spelling Road Race

With a Partner

○ Spelling Tic-Tac-Toe

On Your Own

○ Flip Folder   ○ Spelling Study Strategy

At Home

○ Take Your List Home

✏ Practice the Spelling Pattern

Write two **Pattern Words** with the same vowel sound to finish each sentence. The first letter of each word is there to help you. Then circle **silent e** at the end of the **long i** words you wrote.

Pattern Words

bit
bite
nice
hid
mile
line
hide
five

1–2. A n__ dog doesn't b__ anyone.

_____   _____

_____   _____

3–4. The l__ of cars was a m__ long.

_____   _____

_____   _____

5–6. A snake h__ in the grass and b__ the mouse.

_____   _____

_____   _____

7–8. My f__ cats like to h__ in the barn.

_____   _____

_____   _____

Focus on Writing

A. Proofread the Writing of Others

Proofread the paragraph below. Decide which type of mistake, if any, appears in each underlined part.

> I have fiv fish. did you know fish use
> ①   ②
> fins to swim? I put a shell in my fish tank.
>   ③
> My fish like to hid in it.
>   ④

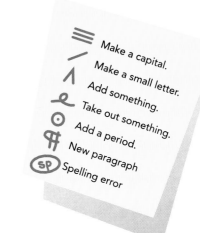

Make a capital.

Make a small letter.

Add something.

Take out something.

Add a period.

New paragraph

ⓢⓅ Spelling error

1. **A** Spelling
   B Capitalization
   C Punctuation
   D No mistake

2. **A** Spelling
   B Capitalization
   C Punctuation
   D No mistake

3. **A** Spelling
   B Capitalization
   C Punctuation
   D No mistake

4. **A** Spelling
   B Capitalization
   C Punctuation
   D No mistake

B. Proofread Your Own Writing

Look in your writing for words with **short i** and **long i** sounds. Correct any misspelled words. Add them to **Words I Need to Know How to Spell**.

C. A Writing Idea: A Description

Make a list of things you might find in a big, dark cave. Use your list to write a paragraph to describe the cave.

Check Your Weekly Progress

▶ **Take the Test**

▶ **Check Your Goal**

▶ **Graph Your Progress**

▶ **Save Missed Words**
Write the words you missed in your list of **Words I Need to Know How to Spell**.

SPELLING PATTERN

11

Long i

Build Your Spelling List

Find Your Pattern Words

Add Teacher Words

Add Your Words

Pattern Words

1. **fine** We had a **fine** time at the zoo.
2. **sky** There were many clouds in the **sky**.
3. **night** Did you see the stars last **night**?
4. **try** Will you **try** to jump rope?
5. **ice** We slipped on the **ice**.
6. **fly** The baby bird is learning to **fly**.
7. **light** Please turn off the **light**.
8. **why** He asked **why** grass is green.

STEP 2 ## Write Your Spelling List

STEP 3 ## Set Your Learning Goal

My spelling list has _____ words.

I like when the teacher adds math words. Knowing those words helps me write better in that class.

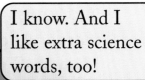

I know. And I like extra science words, too!

STEP 4 Explore the Spelling Pattern

Sorting Words

Sort the **Pattern Words** into three groups. Use the underlined letters in the words below to guide your sort. Write each **Pattern Word** once.

> Try sorting the **Pattern Words** in other ways. Which words have only three letters?

1. sk<u>y</u>

2. n<u>igh</u>t

3. f<u>i</u>n<u>e</u>

STEP 5 Focus on Word Study

Homophones

Words that sound the same but have different meanings and spellings are **homophones**. **Knight** and **night** are homophones. A **knight** is a person, but **night** is the opposite of day.

Match each word with its homophone.

1. bee _____ **a.** hole

2. whole _____ **b.** meet

3. meat _____ **c.** be

▼▼▼▼▼▼▼▼▼▼▼▼▼▼▼

Spelling Pattern

- Listen to **fine**. The **long i** sound is spelled **i**-consonant-**silent e**.

- Listen to **sky**. The **long i** sound is spelled **y**.

- Listen to **night**. The **long i** sound is spelled **igh**.

STEP 6 Practice Your Spelling List Independently

Choose at least three activities to practice your spelling list.

Game Mats

○ Spelling Road Race
○ Spelling Snakes

With a Partner

○ Spelling Tic-Tac-Toe

On Your Own

○ Flip Folder
○ Spelling Study Strategy

At Home

○ Take Your List Home

Practice the Spelling Pattern

Write the **Pattern Word** that fits each clue.
Circle the letters that spell the **long i** sound.

Pattern Words

fine
sky
night
try
ice
fly
light
why

1. Can we do it? Let's __!

2. Look up to see me.

3. A bird can do this, but you can't!

4. You can see the moon at __.

5. If it's not dark, it's __.

6. I am very cold!

7. I start a lot of questions.

8. I mean "very good."

STEP 7 Focus on Writing

A. Hunt Spelling Words in Your Writing

Choose one piece of your latest writing. Work with a spelling partner to look for **long i** words spelled **y, igh,** and **i**-consonant-**silent e**. Use two columns like these to write the words you find.

Make a capital.
Make a small letter.
Add something.
Take out something.
Add a period.
New paragraph
SP Spelling error

Column 1	Column 2
I spelled these **long i** words correctly.	I misspelled these **long i** words.

If you can't find any **long i** words, choose a different piece of your writing.

Add the words you wrote in Column 2 to **Words I Need to Know How to Spell**.

B. A Writing Idea: A Paragraph

What is your favorite time of day? Write a paragraph telling which part of the day you like best and why. Try to get others to agree with your ideas.

STEP 8 Check Your Weekly Progress

► **Take the Test**

► **Check Your Goal**

► **Graph Your Progress**

► **Save Missed Words**
Write the words you missed in your list of **Words I Need to Know How to Spell**.

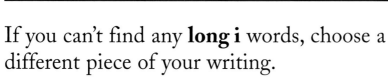

SPELLING PATTERN

12

Short o, Long o

STEP 1 Build Your Spelling List

Find Your Pattern Words

Add Teacher Words

Add Your Words

Pattern Words

1. **not**   I do **not** like peas.
2. **note**   The teacher wrote a **note** on my paper.
3. **love**   Grandpa's letter said, "I **love** you."
4. **trot**   Rosa trained her horse to **trot**.
5. **hop**   Can you **hop** on one foot?
6. **rose**   Jane put a pink **rose** in the vase.
7. **mop**   Use the **mop** to clean the floor.
8. **woke**   Pat **woke** up at seven o'clock.
9. **nose**   The clown has a funny red **nose**.
10. **joke**   Mary told a silly **joke**.
11. **hope**   I **hope** you can come over today.
12. **glove**   The **glove** was too big for my hand.

STEP 2 Write Your Spelling List

STEP 3 Set Your Learning Goal

My spelling list has _____ words.

I can't remember how to spell some words. I'll add them to my list until I get them right!

That's a great idea! You'll write better when you know how to spell the words you want to use.

> You may wish to use **Hands-on Word Sort Cards** and the **Hands-on Word Sort Sheet** for this unit.

STEP 4

Explore the Spelling Pattern
Sorting Words

Read the **Pattern Words** out loud with a partner. Sort each **Pattern Word** by whether it has a **short o** sound, like **not**, or a **long o** sound, like **note**. If a word doesn't fit, write it with the question mark. Write each **Pattern Word** once.

1. n<u>o</u>t

2. n<u>o</u>t<u>e</u>

3. ?

STEP 5

Focus on Word Study
Changes in Spelling

Years ago, the word **hop** was spelled **hoppian**. Later the spelling changed to **hoppen**. Today's spelling—**hop**—is the shortest of all!

Write the **Pattern Word** that came from each old spelling.

1. nosu _____

2. jocus _____

> **Spelling Pattern**
> - Listen to **not**. The **short o** sound is spelled **o**.
> - Listen to **note**. The **long o** sound is spelled **o**-consonant-**silent e**.

STEP 6 Practice Your Spelling List Independently

Choose at least three activities to practice your spelling list.

Game Mats	With a Partner	On Your Own	At Home

○ Funny Faces ○ Spelling Snakes ○ Spelling Tic-Tac-Toe ○ Flip Folder ○ Spelling Study Strategy ○ Take Your List Home

Practice the Spelling Pattern

Each **Pattern Word** is missing the letters that spell the vowel sound. Write the **Pattern Word**. Circle the letters that were missing. Use eight **Pattern Words**.

Pattern Words

not
note
love
trot
hop
rose
mop
woke
nose
joke
hope
glove

1. I saw a frog h_p onto a log.

2. We saw two horses tr_t by.

3. I l_v_ to pet puppies.

4. An elephant has a long n_s_.

5. My dog chews my gl_v_.

6. Chirping birds w_k_ me up.

7. There was a bee on the r_s_.

8. We h_p_ to see a deer.

_____
_____
_____
_____
_____
_____
_____
_____

STEP 7 Focus on Writing

A. Proofread the Writing of Others

Maria used a spelling checker on the computer to proofread her story. Help her choose the correct spelling for the four underlined misspelled words. Write each word she meant.

≡ Make a capital.
/ Make a small letter.
∧ Add something.
ℓ Take out something.
⊙ Add a period.
¶ New paragraph
SP Spelling error

The boy found a <u>noot</u> on the table. It said, "Look under the <u>mopp</u>." At first, the boy did <u>nat</u> see anything there. Then he saw a card that said, "I <u>hoap</u> you have a happy birthday."

1. not   3. nap
   note   nut
   noon   not

2. mop   4. hoop
   mow   hop
   moo   hope

1. _____
2. _____
3. _____
4. _____

B. Proofread Your Own Writing

The **short o** sound in **not** is spelled **o**. The **long o** sound in **note** is spelled **o**-consonant-**silent e**. Look in your writing for words with these sounds. Add misspelled words to **Words I Need to Know How to Spell**.

C. A Writing Idea: A Friendly Note

Write a note to someone you like. Tell what you have been doing in school. Check your spelling.

STEP 8 Check Your Weekly Progress

▶ **Take the Test**

▶ **Check Your Goal**

▶ **Graph Your Progress**

▶ **Save Missed Words**
Write the words you missed in your list of **Words I Need to Know How to Spell**.

SPELLING PATTERN

13

Long o

Build Your Spelling List

Find Your Pattern Words

Add Teacher Words

Add Your Words

Pattern Words

1. **cone**   Would you like an ice cream **cone**?
2. **boat**   We went across the lake in a **boat**.
3. **show**   Diane can **show** you the way.
4. **cold**   It is **cold** and rainy today.
5. **ago**   Two years **ago** I was five years old.
6. **coat**   Will I need to wear my **coat** today?
7. **pole**   We need another **pole** for our tent.
8. **most**   The team with the **most** points wins.
9. **grow**   How tall does corn **grow**?
10. **road** Ron lives on this **road**.
11. **hose** Dan used a **hose** to water the garden.
12. **row**   Is my seat in this **row**?

STEP 2 Write Your Spelling List

STEP 3 Set Your Learning Goal

My spelling list has _____ words.

I hunt for words all the time!

Me, too! I find them at home and on signs. Then I add them to my **Words I Need to Know How to Spell**.

STEP 4 Explore the Spelling Pattern Sorting Words

Find a partner. Sort the **Pattern Words** into four groups. Use the spelling patterns and the words below to guide your sort. If a word doesn't fit with a guide word, write it with the question mark. Write each **Pattern Word** once.

> You may wish to use **Hands-on Word Sort Cards** and the **Hands-on Word Sort Sheet** for this unit.

1. cone	2. show	3. boat	4. ?

STEP 5 Focus on Word Study

Idioms

The word **show** is used in different sayings. If we want things to get started, we might say "Get the **show** on the road." A person who takes charge "runs the **show**."

Write a **Pattern Word** to complete each saying.

1. Don't rock the __ !
   (boat, cone)

2. They got __ feet!
   (pole, cold)

3. Money doesn't __ on
   trees! (row, grow)

▼▼▼▼▼▼▼▼▼▼▼▼
Spelling Pattern
- Listen to **cone**. The **long o** sound is spelled o-consonant-**silent e**.

- Listen to **boat**. The **long o** sound is spelled **oa**.

- Listen to **show**. The **long o** sound is spelled **ow**.

STEP 6 Practice Your Spelling List Independently

Choose at least three activities to practice your spelling list.

Game Mats

○ Funny Faces   ○ Ski Race

With a Partner

○ Spelling Tic-Tac-Toe

On Your Own

○ Flip Folder   ○ Spelling Study Strategy

At Home

○ Take Your List Home

Practice the Spelling Pattern

Write a **Pattern Word** to finish each sentence. Circle the letter or letters that spell the **long o** sound. You'll use eight **Pattern Words**.

Pattern Words

cone
boat
show
cold
ago
coat
pole
most
grow
road
hose
row

1. Many cars are on the __ today.

2. The __ on the fire truck is long.

3. Mom planted a __ of beans.

4. I wear gloves on a __ day.

5. A little __ can push a big ship.

6. Dinosaurs lived a long time __.

7. Dad has a pocket in his __.

8. A fishing __ should bend.

STEP 7 Focus on Writing

A. Hunt Spelling Words in Your Writing

Choose one piece of your latest writing. Work with a spelling partner to look for **long o** words. Use two columns like these to write the words you find.

Make a capital.
Make a small letter.
Add something.
Take out something.
Add a period.
New paragraph
SP Spelling error

Column 1	Column 2
I spelled these **long o** words correctly.	I misspelled these **long o** words.

If you can't find any **long o** words, choose another piece of your writing.

Add the words you wrote in Column 2 to **Words I Need to Know How to Spell**.

B. A Writing Idea: Riddles

Work with a partner to make a list of people you might see in a circus. Use your list to write some riddles. Ask your friends to guess the answers. Here's one to get you started: Who puts on the funniest show? The clowns!

STEP 8 Check Your Weekly Progress

▶ **Take the Test**

▶ **Check Your Goal**

▶ **Graph Your Progress**

▶ **Save Missed Words**
Write the words you missed in your list of **Words I Need to Know How to Spell**.

STEP 1 Build Your Spelling List

Find Your Strategy Words

Add Teacher Words

Add Your Words

Strategy Words

1. **who**   **Who** is at the door?
2. **saw**   We looked, but we never **saw** the rainbow.
3. **want**   I **want** to read this book.
4. **off**   It was dark because the light was **off**.
5. **myself** I did it **myself,** without any help.
6. **how**   Tell me **how** you did that.
7. **fell**   He tripped and **fell** down.
8. **what**   **What** is your name?

STEP 2 Write Your Spelling List

STEP 3 Set Your Learning Goal

My spelling list has _____ words.

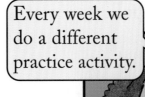

Every week we do a different practice activity.

We're learning all the activities. Then we can choose the ones we want to do.

Explore the Spelling Strategy
Proofread It!

Write the correct word to finish each title.

1. The Day the Tree (Feel, Fell) Down

2. Do You (What, Want) to Know a Secret?

3. (What, Want) a Great Dog!

4. The Case I Solved by (Myself, My Self)

5. The Boy (Saw, Sigh) a Light in the Sky

6. A Girl (How, Who) Likes Frogs

7. She Forgot to Turn the Water (If, Off)

8. (Who, How) Do You Like My Hat?

Focus on Word Study
Related Words

The word **myself** is formed by putting the word **my** with **self**. **Self** is also used with other words to make new words.

Write a "self" word to complete each sentence.

herself   **himself**   **itself**   **yourself**

1. Did you walk home by __?

2. Eva hurt __ on the rocks.

3. My pet bird looks at __ in the mirror.

4. Pedro made the picture by __.

1. _____
2. _____
3. _____
4. _____
5. _____
6. _____
7. _____
8. _____

▼▼▼▼▼▼▼▼▼▼▼▼▼▼
Spelling Strategy
Proofread to check your writing.
■ ■ ■ ■ ■ ■ ■ ■ ■ ■ ■ ■

UNIT **14**   **77**

STEP 6 Practice Your Spelling List Independently

Choose at least three activities to practice your spelling list.

Game Mats

○ Ski Race   ○ Spelling Road Race

With a Partner

○ Spelling Tic-Tac-Toe

On Your Own

○ Flip Folder   ○ Spelling Study Strategy

At Home

○ Take Your List Home

Practice the Spelling Strategy

Read each sentence. Notice each underlined spelling mistake. Write the correct spelling.

Strategy Words

who
saw
want
off
myself
how
fell
what

1. Jack <u>fel</u> down.
_____

2. I can fix it <u>mysellf</u>.
_____

3. I get <u>of</u> the bus here.
_____

4. <u>Howe</u> much are two and two?
_____

5. Do you <u>wannt</u> to read this book?
_____

6. I <u>saww</u> a funny show on TV.
_____

7. <u>Hoo</u> sits next to you?
_____

8. <u>Wut</u> did you buy at the store?
_____

STEP 7 Focus on Writing

A. Proofread the Writing of Others

Check Lila's note for spelling. Find the four words that are spelled wrong. Write the correct spelling of each word.

Dear Tanya,

Hou are you? Do you know wat I did?

I fel off my bike! But I didn't hurt my self.

Your friend,
Lila

1. _____   3. _____

2. _____   4. _____

Make a capital.
Make a small letter.
Add something.
Take out something.
Add a period.
New paragraph
SP Spelling error

B. Proofread Your Own Writing

Proofread your writing so that others can understand what you are saying. Go to your latest piece of writing. Look for spelling mistakes and correct them. Write words you want to learn in **Words I Need to Know How to Spell**.

C. A Writing Idea: A Story

Read the story titles on page 77. Choose one title and write a story to go with it. When you are done, check to be sure you have spelled all the words right.

STEP 8 Check Your Weekly Progress

▶ **Take the Test**

▶ **Check Your Goal**

▶ **Graph Your Progress**

▶ **Save Missed Words**
Write the words you missed in your list of **Words I Need to Know How to Spell**.

SPELLING STRATEGY

15

Words Writers Use

STEP 1 Build Your Spelling List

Find Your Strategy Words

Add Teacher Words

Add Your Words

Strategy Words

1. **little** The **little** puppy fit in my pocket.
2. **many** **Many** people were waiting in line.
3. **after** We went home **after** school.
4. **put** Please **put** your paper on the desk.
5. **house** Nina lives in the blue **house**.
6. **some** **Some** people have red hair.
7. **give** I will **give** you my apple.
8. **very** This book is **very** funny.

STEP 2 Write Your Spelling List

STEP 3 Set Your Learning Goal

My spelling list has _____ words.

If you want to be a better word hunter, read your **Spelling Process Handbook**.

I did! It has some great ideas that help me a lot!

STEP 4 Explore the Spelling Strategy

Check It!

The underlined words below are not spelled right. Write the correct spelling of each word.

1. Please come to my <u>hous</u> at noon.

2. The elephant is a <u>verry</u> large animal.

3. There are <u>meny</u> stars in the sky.

4. I have a <u>litle</u> sister and a big brother.

5. We took <u>sum</u> food on our hike.

6. In the story, what did the giant <u>giv</u> the boy?

7. <u>Aftur</u> you cut the paper, you fold it.

8. <u>Puut</u> a check mark beside your name.

1. _____

2. _____

3. _____

4. _____

5. _____

6. _____

7. _____

8. _____

STEP 5 Focus on Word Study

Word History

The word **little** comes from a word that meant "to stoop." What happens when you stoop, or bend low? You seem to become little!

Look in the puzzle for three words that mean "little." Write the words.

S	M	A	L	L
B	O	Z	I	W
T	I	N	Y	H
S	H	O	R	T

1. _____

2. _____

3. _____

▼▼▼▼▼▼▼▼▼▼▼▼▼▼ Spelling Strategy

It's important to know how to spell words we use often when we write.

STEP 6 Practice Your Spelling List Independently

Choose at least three activities to practice your spelling list.

Game Mats

○ Spelling Road Race   ○ Spelling Snakes

With a Partner

○ Spelling Tic-Tac-Toe

On Your Own

○ Flip Folder   ○ Spelling Study Strategy

At Home

○ Take Your List Home

Practice the Spelling Strategy

The famous author, Phil A. Page, is speaking to your class. Here is his speech. Find his eight spelling mistakes and write the words correctly.

Strategy Words

little
many
after
put
house
some
give
very

Thank you vary much for inviting me. I have written miny books. I know that spelling is important. I will giv you som ideas that work. First, I find a quiet spot in the howse so I can think. I check my words aftir I have finished writing and fix my mistakes. If I putt a littel extra time into checking my spelling, I do better work!

1. _____

2. _____

3. _____

4. _____

5. _____

6. _____

7. _____

8. _____

Focus on Writing

A. Proofread the Writing of Others

Proofread this paragraph on how to make a beanbag. Decide which type of mistake, if any, appears in each underlined part.

> You need cloth, a needle with a long piece
> of yarn in it, and beans. Cut out a big half
>   ①
> circle and a littal circle. Sew the half circle to
>   ②
> make a cone. Put in as minny beans as you
>   ③
> can. Sew on the small circle for the bottom
>   ④

1. A Spelling
   B Capitalization
   C Punctuation
   D No mistake

3. A Spelling
   B Capitalization
   C Punctuation
   D No mistake

2. A Spelling
   B Capitalization
   C Punctuation
   D No mistake

4. A Spelling
   B Capitalization
   C Punctuation
   D No mistake

B. Proofread Your Own Writing

Look for misspelled words in your writing. Write them in **Words I Need to Know How to Spell**.

C. A Writing Idea: A Paragraph

Think about a building you know. Write a paragraph that tells what it looks like.

Step 8

Check Your Weekly Progress

▶ **Take the Test**

▶ **Check Your Goal**

▶ **Graph Your Progress**

▶ **Save Missed Words**
Write the words you missed in your list of **Words I Need to Know How to Spell**.

SPELLING PATTERN

16

s Blends

STEP 1

Build Your Spelling List

Find Your Pattern Words

Add Teacher Words

Add Your Words

Pattern Words

1. **say**   What did you **say**?
2. **stay**   Let's **stay** here until Dad comes.
3. **slow**   Please **slow** down and wait for me.
4. **pot**   The soup in the **pot** is ready to eat.
5. **low**   The children sat on **low** chairs.
6. **spot**   There is a wet **spot** on the floor.
7. **start**   The bike race will **start** at noon.
8. **snow**   The **snow** covered the ground.

STEP 2

Write Your Spelling List

STEP 3

Set Your Learning Goal

My spelling list has _____ words.

A practice test helps me make sure I'm ready for the final test.

I get ready by practicing with a friend.

Try sorting the **Pattern Words** in other ways. Which words have an **o**?

STEP 4 Explore the Spelling Pattern

Sorting Words

Sort the **Pattern Words** into two groups—words that start with one consonant and words that start with two consonants. Make sure you write each **Pattern Word** once.

1. <u>s</u>ay

2. <u>st</u>ay

STEP 5 Focus on Word Study

Idioms

Many **Pattern Words** are used in idioms, or sayings. For example, the saying "You can **say** that again!" means "I agree with you." The saying "**Stay** put!" means "Don't move."

Write a **Pattern Word** to complete each saying.

1. in trouble, or "in a bad __" (slow, spot)

2. to hide, or "lie __" (low, start)

3. to give too much work, or " __ under" (pot, snow)

1. _____

2. _____

3. _____

STEP 6 Practice Your Spelling List Independently

Choose at least three activities to practice your spelling list.

Game Mats

○ Funny Faces   ○ Spelling Snakes

With a Partner

○ Spelling Tic-Tac-Toe

On Your Own

○ Flip Folder   ○ Spelling Study Strategy

At Home

○ Take Your List Home

Practice the Spelling Pattern

Write a **Pattern Word** to answer each riddle.

Pattern Words

say
stay
slow
pot
low
spot
start
snow

1. I begin like **stop**.
   I rhyme with **day**.

   _____

2. I begin like **slip**.
   I rhyme with **mow**.

   _____

3. I begin like **spell**.
   I rhyme with **hot**.

   _____

4. I begin like **step**.
   I rhyme with **part**.

   _____

5. I begin like **sit**.
   I rhyme with **may**.

   _____

6. I begin like **like**.
   I rhyme with **blow**.

   _____

7. I begin like **pen**.
   I rhyme with **dot**.

   _____

8. I begin like **snake**.
   I rhyme with **slow**.

   _____

Focus on Writing

A. Proofread the Writing of Others

Find the four spelling mistakes in Stan's tongue twisters. Write each word correctly.

1. Stai and stir the stew.

2. I spy a spott on the spoon.

3. Saye seven silly sayings.

4. Sneezy sneezed in the snoe.

1. _____   3. _____

2. _____   4. _____

Make a capital.
Make a small letter.
Add something.
Take out something.
Add a period.
New paragraph
SP Spelling error

B. Proofread Your Own Writing

The consonant **s** often works alone or in a blend with another consonant. Look for words in your latest piece of writing that begin with **s** or an **s** blend such as **st, sl, sp,** or **sn.** Correct any words you misspelled. Write the words in **Words I Need to Know How to Spell**.

C. A Writing Idea: A Description

What do you know about snow? Have you ever seen real snow outdoors? Or have you seen it on TV? Think about what snow looks like, how it feels, and what you can do with it. Write a paragraph to describe snow.

Check Your Weekly Progress

▶ **Take the Test**

▶ **Check Your Goal**

▶ **Graph Your Progress**

▶ **Save Missed Words**
Write the words you missed in your list of **Words I Need to Know How to Spell**.

Check Your

✓ Check Your Spelling

Review Test

1 _____

2 _____

3 _____

4 _____

5 _____

6 _____

7 _____

8 _____

9 _____

10 _____

11 _____

12 _____

Here is a fun way to review your progress on spelling patterns. First, take the review test your teacher will give you. Then, check your test.

Progress

Which words did you spell correctly? Use the **Spelling Pattern Mastery Chart** to find your mastery level for each spelling pattern.

Spelling Pattern Mastery Chart

Pattern	All Correct	None Correct
Short i, Long i 2 6		
Long i 3 9		
Short o, Long o 4 8 11		
Long o 5 12		
s Blends 1 7 10		

All Correct: Pattern Mastered
None Correct: Keep Working on the Pattern

✔ Check Your Writing

Work with a partner to check your writing for words that match each pattern. Write misspelled words in your **Words I Need to Know How to Spell**.

SPELLING PATTERN

17

Consonant Blends With l

STEP 1 Build Your Spelling List

Find Your Pattern Words

Add Teacher Words

Add Your Words

Pattern Words

1. **black**   We named our **black** cat Inky.
2. **club**   We have a reading **club** at school.
3. **flag**   The **flag** is blowing in the wind.
4. **glad**   I'm **glad** you are in my class.
5. **play**   We can **play** softball after lunch.
6. **plant**   Who will water this **plant** for me?
7. **clap**   Let's **clap** our hands for the winners!
8. **glass**   Would you like a **glass** of milk?

STEP 2 Write Your Spelling List

STEP 3 Set Your Learning Goal

My spelling list has _____ words.

Building my spelling list helps me think about the spelling patterns I'm learning.

Me, too! Thinking about my spelling words is helping me write better.

STEP 4

Explore the Spelling Pattern
Sorting Words

Sort the **Pattern Words** into five groups. Use the words below to guide your sort. Make sure you write each **Pattern Word** once.

Try sorting the words in other ways. How many words are spelled with only four letters?

1. <u>bl</u>ack

3. <u>fl</u>ag

5. <u>pl</u>ay

2. <u>cl</u>ub

4. <u>gl</u>ad

▼▼▼▼▼▼▼▼▼▼▼▼▼▼

Spelling Pattern

Remember that consonants can work together in blends. Listen to **black, club, flag, glad,** and **play**. The consonant blends in these words are **bl, cl, fl, gl,** and **pl**.

STEP 5

Focus on Word Study
Making New Words

Sometimes you can make a whole new word just by changing or dropping only one letter of a word. For example, if you take the **l** out of **club,** you make the word **cub**.

Take away the **l** from each of these **Pattern Words**. Then write the new words you made.

1. clap _____

3. play _____

2. black _____

STEP 6 Practice Your Spelling List Independently

Choose at least three activities to practice your spelling list.

Game Mats

○ Funny Faces   ○ Ski Race

With a Partner

○ Spelling Tic-Tac-Toe

On Your Own

○ Flip Folder   ○ Spelling Study Strategy

At Home

○ Take Your List Home

Practice the Spelling Pattern

What letters are missing in each **Pattern Word**? Write the whole word. Circle the letters that were missing.

Pattern Words

black
club
flag
glad
play
plant
clap
glass

1. __ - __ - a - c - k   _____

2. __ - __ - a - p   _____

3. __ - __ - u - b   _____

4. __ - __ - a - s - s   _____

5. __ - __ - a - d   _____

6. __ - __ - a - g   _____

7. __ - __ - a - y   _____

8. __ - __ - a - n - t   _____

Focus on Writing

A. Proofread the Writing of Others

Find the four words that are not spelled right in Rob's story. Write the correct spelling of each one.

My friends and I have a secret klub. We meet there after school and blay games. We made our own flagg. It is white with a plack star for each of us.

1. _____

2. _____

3. _____

4. _____

Make a capital.
Make a small letter.
Add something.
Take out something.
Add a period.
New paragraph
SP Spelling error

B. Proofread Your Own Writing

Many words begin with **bl, cl, fl, gl,** and **pl.** Check your latest piece of writing. Did you spell words with consonant blends correctly? Write misspelled words in **Words I Need to Know How to Spell**.

C. A Writing Idea: A Paragraph

Countries have flags. States have flags. Even some families have flags! Draw a flag for your family. Then write a short paragraph to tell why you chose this flag.

STEP 8

Check Your Weekly Progress

► **Take the Test**

► **Check Your Goal**

► **Graph Your Progress**

► **Save Missed Words**
Write the words you missed in your list of **Words I Need to Know How to Spell**.

SPELLING PATTERN

18

Consonant Blends With r

STEP 1 Build Your Spelling List

Find Your Pattern Words

Add Teacher Words

Add Your Words

Pattern Words

1. **bring**   Please **bring** the book to me.
2. **dress**   Alice wore a blue **dress** to the party.
3. **frog**   Tammy has a pet **frog**.
4. **green**   I will draw **green** leaves on the tree.
5. **crack**   There is a **crack** in the window.
6. **brush**   I **brush** my teeth three times a day.
7. **train**   I can hear a **train** coming.
8. **drive**   Can your mom **drive** us to the store?

STEP 2 Write Your Spelling List

STEP 3 Set Your Learning Goal

My spelling list has _____ words.

I use the **Pattern Words** list to see the spelling pattern in a group of words.

Right! Then I can spell other words with the same pattern.

STEP 4

Explore the Spelling Pattern
Sorting Words

> Try sorting the words in other ways. Which words end with just one consonant?

Making a word sort can help you think about words. Sort the **Pattern Words** into six groups. Use the words below to guide your sort. Make sure you write each **Pattern Word** once.

1. bring

3. dress

5. frog

2. green

4. crack

6. train

STEP 5

Focus on Word Study
Changes in Spelling

The English word for **frog** has been almost the same for hundreds of years! First our name for this little green animal was spelled **frogge**, then **froge**, and finally **frog**.

Write the **Pattern Word** that each of these early spellings became.

1. trayne, trayn _____

2. grœni, grene _____

3. broce, brousse _____

▼▼▼▼▼▼▼▼▼▼▼▼▼▼▼▼▼▼

Spelling Pattern
Listen to **bring, dress, frog,** and **green.** The consonant blends in these words are **br, dr, fr,** and **gr.**

STEP 6 Practice Your Spelling List Independently

Choose at least three activities to practice your spelling list.

Game Mats

○ Ski Race   ○ Spelling Road Race

With a Partner

○ Spelling Tic-Tac-Toe

On Your Own

○ Flip Folder   ○ Spelling Study Strategy

At Home

○ Take Your List Home

Practice the Spelling Pattern

Write the **Pattern Word** correctly to complete each sentence. Circle the letters that were missing.

Pattern Words

bring
dress
frog
green
crack
brush
train
drive

1. I found a big __een frog in a pond on my vacation. _____

2. I put it in a pocket of my __ess. _____

3. I had my __ush in the other pocket. _____

4. I wanted to __ing the frog home. _____

5. I knew the frog wouldn't mind the long __ive in the car. _____

6. But Mom said we had to take a __ain home instead. _____

7. So I put the __og in a big jar to carry it back to the pond. _____

8. I dropped the jar, and it got a big __ack! The frog hopped out. _____

STEP 7 Focus on Writing

A. Proofread the Writing of Others

Proofread the paragraph below. Decide which type of mistake, if any, appears in each underlined part.

Can a <u>frog wear a dress.</u> No. Can a frog
          ①

<u>prive a train?</u> No. <u>Can a frog</u> paint with a
     ②   ③

brush? No. What can a <u>grog do?</u> Croak!
                           ④

1. A Spelling
   B Capitalization
   C Punctuation
   D No mistake

2. A Spelling
   B Capitalization
   C Punctuation
   D No mistake

3. A Spelling
   B Capitalization
   C Punctuation
   D No mistake

4. A Spelling
   B Capitalization
   C Punctuation
   D No mistake

B. Proofread Your Own Writing

Find your latest piece of writing. Did you spell the words with **br, cr, dr, fr, gr,** and **tr** correctly?

C. A Writing Idea: Tongue Twisters

Tongue twisters can be fun! Make a list of words that start with one of these consonant blends: **br, cr, dr, fr, gr, tr.** Then use the words to write a tongue twister.

STEP 8 Check Your Weekly Progress

► **Take the Test**

► **Check Your Goal**

► **Graph Your Progress**

► **Save Missed Words**
Write the words you missed in your list of **Words I Need to Know How to Spell**.

STEP 1

Build Your Spelling List

Find Your Pattern Words

Add Teacher Words

Add Your Words

Pattern Words

1. **park**   Let's meet at the **park** after school.
2. **corn**   My aunt grows **corn** on her farm.
3. **story** Mr. Washington read a **story** to us.
4. **far**   Is your family moving **far** away?
5. **horse** I rode a **horse** at the fair.
6. **hard**   This clay is too **hard** to use.
7. **part**   Would you like **part** of this apple?
8. **north** I live **north** of the school.

STEP 2

Write Your Spelling List

STEP 3

Set Your Learning Goal

My spelling list has _____ words.

The teacher sometimes adds words to our spelling lists, like the Red List or the Blue List from **More Words for Hungry Word Hunters.**

Yes. Our teacher even adds social studies words, too.

STEP 4 Explore the Spelling Pattern
Sorting Words

Try sorting the words in other ways. Which words end with three consonants?

Making a word sort can help you think about words. Sort the **Pattern Words** into two groups. Use the words below to guide your sort. Make sure you write each **Pattern Word** once.

1. park

2. corn

Spelling Pattern

- Listen to **park**. The vowel sound is made by **a** and **r** working together.

- Listen to **corn**. The vowel sound is made by **o** and **r** working together.

STEP 5 Focus on Word Study
Multiple Meanings

Some words—like **park**—have more than one meaning. For example, you know that a **park** is a place with trees and grass. Also, a driver can **park** a car in a driveway.

One **Pattern Word** fits both blanks in each sentence below. Write the word.

1. You can have a __ in your hair and a __ in a play.

2. You can tell a __ and you can climb to the third __ in a building.

STEP 6 Practice Your Spelling List Independently

Choose at least three activities to practice your spelling list.

Game Mats	With a Partner	On Your Own	At Home

○ Spelling Road Race ○ Spelling Snakes   ○ Spelling Tic-Tac-Toe   ○ Flip Folder ○ Spelling Study Strategy   ○ Take Your List Home

Practice the Spelling Pattern

Write the **Pattern Word** correctly to complete each sentence. Circle the letters that were missing.

Pattern Words

park
corn
story
far
horse
hard
part
north

1. The gray h_se won the race.

2. I read a great st_y in school!

3. I could only eat p_t of my lunch.

4. We rode n_th on our vacation.

5. How f_ is your house from school?

6. Let's go to the p_k to play ball.

7. My favorite food is c_n on the cob.

8. That math test was too h_d!

STEP 7 Focus on Writing

A. Hunt Spelling Words in Your Writing

Choose some of your latest writing. Work with a spelling partner to look for words with **ar** and **or**. Use two columns like these to write the words you find.

Make a capital.
Make a small letter.
Add something.
Take out something.
Add a period.
New paragraph
SP Spelling error

Column 1	Column 2
I spelled these **ar** and **or** words correctly.	I misspelled these **ar** and **or** words.

Add the words you wrote in Column 2 to **Words I Need to Know How to Spell**.

B. A Writing Idea: An Ad

Think of your favorite park—it can be real or make-believe. Make a list of things you might see and do there. Use your list to write an ad about the park. Make it sound like a fun place to visit! Then proofread your writing.

STEP 8 Check Your Weekly Progress

▶ **Take the Test**

▶ **Check Your Goal**

▶ **Graph Your Progress**

▶ **Save Missed Words**
Write the words you missed in your list of **Words I Need to Know How to Spell**.

SPELLING PATTERN
20
r With Vowels

STEP 1 Build Your Spelling List

Find Your Pattern Words

Add Teacher Words

Add Your Words

Pattern Words

1. **from**   Marty got a letter **from** her brother.
2. **first**   Carol was the **first** player to score.
3. **form**   Please write your name on this **form**.
4. **three**   Don's sister is **three** years old.
5. **farm**   Cows and pigs live on the **farm**.
6. **born**   These kittens were **born** last week.
7. **girl**   There is a new **girl** in our class.
8. **there**   We'll put the table over **there**.

STEP 2 Write Your Spelling List

STEP 3 Set Your Learning Goal

My spelling list has _____ words.

When I check my writing, especially in reading and science, I find words I need to know how to spell.

How do you find words for your spelling list?

STEP 4

Explore the Spelling Pattern
Sorting Words

> Try sorting the words in other ways. How many words start with **f**?

Making a word sort can help you think about words. Sort the **Pattern Words** into two groups. Use the words below to guide your sort. Make sure you write each **Pattern Word** once.

1. from
(r before vowel)

2. first
(r after vowel)

STEP 5

Focus on Word Study
Spelling and Meaning

Spelling words correctly is important. Putting just one letter in the wrong place can change the meaning of a word. A **girl** is a person, but a **grill** is used to cook food.

Move one letter in each **Pattern Word** to get a new word. Write the new word.

1. three _____

2. form _____

▼▼▼▼▼▼▼▼▼▼▼▼▼▼

Spelling Pattern

- Listen to **from**. The **r** comes before the vowel.

- Listen to **first**. The **r** comes after the vowel.

- Listen carefully to words with **r** to hear if the **r** comes before or after the vowel.

STEP 6 Practice Your Spelling List Independently

Choose at least three activities to practice your spelling list.

Game Mats

○ Funny Faces   ○ Spelling Snakes

With a Partner

○ Spelling Tic-Tac-Toe

On Your Own

○ Flip Folder   ○ Spelling Study Strategy

At Home

○ Take Your List Home

Practice the Spelling Pattern

Write the **Pattern Word** that comes in A-B-C order between the words in each pair. Circle the **r** in each word you wrote.

Pattern Words

from
first
form
three
farm
born
girl
there

1. book, __, brake _____

2. fan, __, from _____

3. them, __, three _____

4. fork, __, fun _____

5. game, __, gum _____

6. fall, __, fist _____

7. there, __, toad _____

8. for, __, from _____

Focus on Writing

A. Proofread the Writing of Others

Sue made four spelling mistakes in her journal entry. Write the correct spelling of each misspelled word.

October 10

A new gurl joined our class today. Her

frist name is Amy. Amy comes form

Kansas. She was boren on a farm.

1. _____   3. _____

2. _____   4. _____

Make a capital.
Make a small letter.
Add something.
Take out something.
Add a period.
New paragraph
Spelling error

B. Proofread Your Own Writing

Listen carefully to words with **r** to hear whether the **r** comes before or after the vowel. Look for words with **r** in your writing. Check to be sure the **r** is in the right place. Write misspelled words in **Words I Need to Know How to Spell**.

C. A Writing Idea: A Description

Make a list of animals that live on a farm. Choose one animal. Write a paragraph to describe how it looks and sounds. You might want to draw a picture of the animal.

Check Your Weekly Progress

▶ **Take the Test**

▶ **Check Your Goal**

▶ **Graph Your Progress**

▶ **Save Missed Words**
Write the words you missed in your list of **Words I Need to Know How to Spell**.

SPELLING PATTERN

21

k Sound: k, ck

STEP 1 Build Your Spelling List

Find Your Pattern Words

Add Teacher Words

Add Your Words

Pattern Words

1.	**bike**	Do you ride your **bike** to school?
2.	**duck**	We fed a **duck** at the pond.
3.	**milk**	I would like some **milk,** please.
4.	**took**	Dad **took** us to the zoo today.
5.	**talk**	My baby sister can **talk**.
6.	**work**	Mom goes to **work** early.
7.	**rock**	Jerry threw a **rock** into the lake.
8.	**wake**	Loud noises will **wake** the baby.
9.	**back**	When will Mr. Gomez be **back**?
10.	**make**	I can **make** a castle in the sand.
11.	**truck**	Grandpa's **truck** is bright red.
12.	**sick**	Linda was **sick** on Monday.

STEP 2 Write Your Spelling List

STEP 3 Set Your Learning Goal

My spelling list has _____ words.

> Use a blank bookmark. Write down words you want to spell. Then write them in **Words I Need to Know How to Spell**.

> How do I hunt words when I read?

STEP 4 Explore the Spelling Pattern
Sorting Words

You may wish to use **Hands-on Word Sort Cards** and the **Hands-on Word Sort Sheet** for this unit.

Find a partner. Sort the **Pattern Words** into two groups. Use the words below to guide your sort. Write each **Pattern Word** once.

1. mil_k_

2. du_ck_

STEP 5 Focus on Word Study
Clipped Words

Bike is short for **bicycle**. A short form of a longer word is a **clipped word**.

A **nickname** is a kind of clipped word. **Kim** is a short form of **Kimberly**. Write a short form, or nickname, for these names.

1. Susan

2. Michael

▼ ▼ ▼ ▼ ▼ ▼ ▼ ▼ ▼ ▼ ▼ ▼

Spelling Pattern

The **k** sound at the end of a word is usually spelled with **k,** as in **bike, milk,** and **took,** or **ck,** as in **duck.**

STEP 6 Practice Your Spelling List Independently

Choose at least three activities to practice your spelling list.

Game Mats

○ Funny Faces   ○ Ski Race

With a Partner

○ Spelling Tic-Tac-Toe

On Your Own

○ Flip Folder   ○ Spelling Study Strategy

At Home

○ Take Your List Home

Practice the Spelling Pattern

Each underlined word rhymes with a **Pattern Word**. Write the rhyming **Pattern Word**. You'll use eight **Pattern Words**.

Pattern Words

bike
duck
milk
took
talk
work
rock
wake
back
make
truck
sick

1. Let's take a <u>walk</u> and have a __.

2. The fresh __ was as smooth as <u>silk</u>.

3. Would you rather <u>hike</u> or ride a __?

4. Ari __ his coat off the <u>hook</u>.

5. Someone broke the <u>lock</u> with a __.

6. The __ got <u>stuck</u> in the mud.

7. <u>Take</u> care not to __ the baby.

8. Poor <u>Dick</u> felt very __.

Focus on Writing

A. Hunt Spelling Words in Your Writing

Choose one piece of your latest writing. Work with a spelling partner to look for words that end with the **k** sound spelled **k** or **ck**. Use two columns like these to write the words you find.

= Make a capital.
/ Make a small letter.
∧ Add something.
℮ Take out something.
⊙ Add a period.
ℋ New paragraph
(SP) Spelling error

Column 1	Column 2
I spelled these words with the **k** sound correctly.	I misspelled these words with the **k** sound.

If you can't find any words with the **k** sound, choose a different piece of your writing.

Add the words you wrote in Column 2 to **Words I Need to Know How to Spell**.

B. A Writing Idea: A Letter

What could you say to a sick friend to make that friend feel better? Write a letter to a real or make-believe friend who is sick. Check your spelling.

STEP 8

Check Your Weekly Progress

▶ **Take the Test**

▶ **Check Your Goal**

▶ **Graph Your Progress**

▶ **Save Missed Words**
Write the words you missed in your list of **Words I Need to Know How to Spell**.

SPELLING PATTERN

22

Consonants: ch, sh

 STEP 1

Build Your Spelling List

Find Your Pattern Words

Add Teacher Words

Add Your Words

Pattern Words

1. **child**   My dad was once a **child** like me.
2. **ship**   Have you ever sailed on a **ship**?
3. **much**   There is too **much** milk in my cup.
4. **fish**   I counted twenty **fish** in the tank.
5. **each**   Please give a book to **each** person.
6. **wash**   **Wash** your hands before you eat.
7. **shoe**   Anthony lost his **shoe** during the race.
8. **reach**   Can you **reach** the top shelf?

STEP 2

Write Your Spelling List

STEP 3

Set Your Learning Goal

My spelling list has _____ words.

Do you have a favorite game mat?

I used to play **Spelling Snakes** all the time, but now I love **Funny Faces!**

STEP 4 Explore the Spelling Pattern
Sorting Words

Sort the **Pattern Words** into four groups. Use the words below to guide your sort. Make sure you write each **Pattern Word** once.

1. <u>ch</u>ild

_____
- - - - - - - - - - - -
_____

2. mu<u>ch</u>

_____
- - - - - - - - - - - -
_____
- - - - - - - - - - - -
_____

3. <u>sh</u>ip

_____
- - - - - - - - - - - -
_____
- - - - - - - - - - - -
_____

4. fi<u>sh</u>

_____
- - - - - - - - - - - -
_____
- - - - - - - - - - - -
_____

Try sorting the words in other ways. Which words name a person, a place, or a thing?

STEP 5 Focus on Word Study
Compound Words

What kind of shoes do horses wear? Horses wear horseshoes. **Horseshoes** is a compound word made of two words.

Match one word from each column to make a compound word. Write the compound words.

_____
- - - - - - - - - - - -

1. bath   port   _____

_____
- - - - - - - - - - - -

2. air   tub   _____

▼▼▼▼▼▼▼▼▼▼▼▼▼
Spelling Pattern

- Listen to **child** and **much**. The sound at the start of **child** and the end of **much** is spelled **ch**.

- Listen to **ship** and **fish**. The sound at the start of **ship** and the end of **fish** is spelled **sh**.

· · · · · · · · · · · · · · · · · · ·

STEP 6 Practice Your Spelling List Independently

Choose at least three activities to practice your spelling list.

Game Mats	With a Partner	On Your Own	At Home

○ Ski Race ○ Spelling Road Race ○ Spelling Tic-Tac-Toe ○ Flip Folder ○ Spelling Study Strategy ○ Take Your List Home

Practice the Spelling Pattern

Use two **Pattern Words** to finish each sentence. Then read the sentences aloud to be sure they make sense.

Pattern Words

child
ship
much
fish
each
wash
shoe
reach

1–2. Those muddy sneakers should go to a __ __.

_____   _____

3–4. The shelf is __ too high to __.

_____   _____

5–6. My father is a sailor on a __ __.

_____   _____

7–8. __ __ has a can of paint.

_____   _____

STEP 7 Focus on Writing

A. Proofread the Writing of Others

Find the four words that are misspelled in Tony's letter. Write the correct spelling of each one.

Dear Aunt Liz,

Mom and Dad took me on a big chip.
We sailed so far I couldn't reash land if I
tried to swim. Eech day we saw something
new. One day we saw the biggest fissh in
the world!

Love,
Tony

1. _____   3. _____

2. _____   4. _____

Make a capital.
Make a small letter.
Add something.
Take out something.
Add a period.
New paragraph
SP Spelling error

B. Proofread Your Own Writing

The letters **ch** and **sh** can come at the start or the end of words. Look for words with **ch** and **sh** in your writing. Are they spelled correctly? Add misspelled words to **Words I Need to Know How to Spell**.

C. A Writing Idea: A Paragraph

What do you know about fish? Write a paragraph that tells something about fish. Proofread your writing before you share it.

STEP 8 Check Your Weekly Progress

► **Take the Test**

► **Check Your Goal**

► **Graph Your Progress**

► **Save Missed Words**
Write the words you missed in your list of **Words I Need to Know How to Spell**.

SPELLING PATTERN

23

Consonants: th

STEP 1

Build Your Spelling List

Find Your Pattern Words

Add Teacher Words

Add Your Words

Pattern Words

1. **them**   May I go with **them** to the park?
2. **thank** **Thank** you for the presents!
3. **these** Do you like **these** pink shoes?
4. **other** Robert ate the **other** apple.
5. **than**   Your book is bigger **than** mine.
6. **both**   We can **both** play this game.
7. **they**   **They** will visit us after lunch.
8. **that**   Please give **that** book to Lee.

STEP 2

Write Your Spelling List

STEP 3

Set Your Learning Goal

My spelling list has _____ words.

I use the **Spelling Process Handbook** for practice test directions.

I like to practice test with a friend.

STEP 4

Explore the Spelling Pattern
Sorting Words

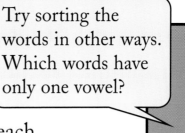

Try sorting the words in other ways. Which words have only one vowel?

Sort the **Pattern Words** into three groups. (Think about where **th** comes in each word.) Use the words below to guide your sort. Write each **Pattern Word** once.

1. <u>them</u>

2. <u>other</u>

3. <u>both</u>

STEP 5

Focus on Word Study
Related Words

The words **thank** and **think** have very different meanings, but they look a lot alike. Both **thank** and **think** come from an old word meaning "thought." If you have a nice thought about someone, she may want to thank you!

Two other **Pattern Words** are related—**they** and **them**. Write **they** or **them** to complete each sentence.

1. __ will come with us.

2. Please take __ home.

▼▼▼▼▼▼▼▼▼▼▼▼▼▼
Spelling Pattern

• Listen to **them**. The sound at the start of **them** is spelled **th**.

• Listen to **thank**. The sound at the start of **thank** is also spelled **th**.

STEP 6 Practice Your Spelling List Independently

Choose at least three activities to practice your spelling list.

Game Mats

○ Spelling Road Race   ○ Spelling Snakes

With a Partner

○ Spelling Tic-Tac-Toe

On Your Own

○ Flip Folder   ○ Spelling Study Strategy

At Home

○ Take Your List Home

Practice the Spelling Pattern

Write the **Pattern Word** that best fits the meaning of the sentence. Circle **th** in each word you wrote.

Pattern Words

them
thank
these
other
than
both
they
that

1. We sent __ some flowers.

2. Where is your __ mitten?

3. I am taller __ you.

4. __ jeans are new.

5. Did you see __ big, red balloon?

6. Why are __ singing a song now?

7. Did you __ her for helping you?

8. Mother gave __ of us a pear.

STEP 7 Focus on Writing

A. Proofread the Writing of Others

Proofread Ruth's speech. Decide which type of mistake, if any, appears in each underlined part.

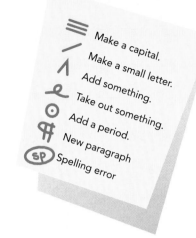

Make a capital.
Make a small letter.
Add something.
Take out something.
Add a period.
New paragraph
SP Spelling error

Look at <u>theeze</u> pictures. They show how
①
messy the <u>park is The trees</u> are sick. We
②
have to <u>save them. doing</u> that is important
③
to everyone. <u>Tank you for</u> coming here to
④
help us.

1. A Spelling
   B Capitalization
   C Punctuation
   D No mistake

2. A Spelling
   B Capitalization
   C Punctuation
   D No mistake

3. A Spelling
   B Capitalization
   C Punctuation
   D No mistake

4. A Spelling
   B Capitalization
   C Punctuation
   D No mistake

B. Proofread Your Own Writing

Look for **th** words in your writing. Correct misspelled words. Write them in **Words I Need to Know How to Spell**.

C. A Writing Idea: A Letter

Did someone help you lately? Write a thank-you letter. Tell why you are writing. Check your spelling and send the letter.

STEP 8 Check Your Weekly Progress

▶ **Take the Test**

▶ **Check Your Goal**

▶ **Graph Your Progress**

▶ **Save Missed Words**
Write the words you missed in your list of **Words I Need to Know How to Spell**.

SPELLING STRATEGY

24

Family Names

STEP 1 Build Your Spelling List

Find Your Strategy Words

Add Teacher Words

Add Your Words

Strategy Words

1. **sister**   Sara is my only **sister**.
2. **father**   Dan's **father** is our soccer coach.
3. **uncle**   Lee's **uncle** always tells jokes.
4. **daddy**   I call my father "**daddy**."
5. **mother**   My **mother** works downtown.
6. **aunt**   Does your **aunt** live nearby?
7. **mommy**   The baby wants her **mommy**.
8. **brother**   Do you have a **brother**?

STEP 2 Write Your Spelling List

STEP 3 Set Your Learning Goal

My spelling list has _____ words.

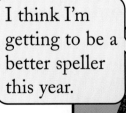

I think I'm getting to be a better speller this year.

I graph my score every week, so I *know* I'm getting better.

Explore the Spelling Strategy
Completing a Chart

Write **Strategy Words** to make a chart of family names.

Names for Women and Girls	Names for Men and Boys
1. _____	5. _____
2. _____	6. _____
3. _____	7. _____
4. _____	8. _____

Focus on Word Study
Idioms

Someone who says "Oh, brother!" isn't talking to his brother. He's using an **idiom,** or a special saying, that means "I can't believe that!"

Write **boy** or **dog** to complete each idiom.

1. Oh __! I want to go, too!

   _____

2. It's so late I'm __ tired!

   _____

Spelling Strategy

People in families have special names for the roles they play. Knowing how to spell these names will help you when you write about your family.

STEP 6 Practice Your Spelling List Independently

Choose at least three activities to practice your spelling list.

Game Mats	With a Partner	On Your Own	At Home

○ Spelling Snakes   ○ Funny Faces   ○ Spelling Tic-Tac-Toe   ○ Flip Folder   ○ Spelling Study Strategy   ○ Take Your List Home

Practice the Spelling Strategy

Write the **Strategy Word** that answers each clue.

Strategy Words

sister
father
uncle
daddy
mother
aunt
mommy
brother

1. She is married to your uncle. _____

2. This is another word for father. _____

3. This boy has the same parents you do. _____

4. You might call her maman, mamá, mommy, or mom. _____

5. He is married to your aunt. _____

6. This is another word for mother. _____

7. This girl has the same parents you do. _____

8. You might call him papá, pop, daddy, or dad. _____

STEP 7 Focus on Writing

A. Proofread the Writing of Others

Find the four misspelled words in Nan's riddle. Write the correct spelling of each word.

Mothr, mom, and ma. Fathre, dad, and pa.

Sis and sistr, bruther and bro.

How many people are there?

The answer is below.

Make a capital.
Make a small letter.
Add something.
Take out something.
Add a period.
New paragraph
SP Spelling error

1. _____

2. _____

3. _____

4. _____

Answer: 4

B. Proofread Your Own Writing

Family members have special names that tell how they are related to other family members. Check your writing for family names. Correct names that are not spelled right.

C. A Writing Idea: A Description

Write about the members of your family. Tell the name of each person. Explain how each person is related to you. Write something about each person, such as what he or she likes to do.

STEP 8 Check Your Weekly Progress

▶ **Take the Test**

▶ **Check Your Goal**

▶ **Graph Your Progress**

▶ **Save Missed Words**
Write the words you missed in your list of **Words I Need to Know How to Spell**.

✓ Check Your Spelling

Review Test

1 _____

2 _____

3 _____

4 _____

5 _____

6 _____

7 _____

8 _____

9 _____

10 _____

11 _____

12 _____

Here is a fun way to review your progress on spelling patterns. First, take the review test your teacher will give you. Then, check your test.

Progress

Which words did you spell correctly? Use the **Spelling Pattern Mastery Chart** to find your mastery level for each spelling pattern.

Spelling Pattern Mastery Chart

Pattern	All Correct	None Correct
l Blends 1 3		
r Blends 4 9		
ar, or 5 12		
r With Vowels 6 8		
k Sounds: k, ck 11		
ch, sh 7 10		
th 2		

All Correct: Pattern Mastered
None Correct: Keep Working on the Pattern

✓ Check Your Writing

Work with a partner to check your writing for words that match each pattern. Write misspelled words in your **Words I Need to Know How to Spell**.

SPELLING PATTERN

25

Endings: -ed

STEP 1 Build Your Spelling List

Find Your Pattern Words

Add Teacher Words

Add Your Words

Pattern Words

1. **looked**   Maria **looked** out the window.
2. **played**   We **played** baseball all afternoon.
3. **needed**   Jan **needed** new shoes.
4. **bent**   The trees **bent** low in the wind.
5. **wanted**   The baby **wanted** his father.
6. **asked**   She **asked** me to come to the party.
7. **planted**   Our class **planted** flowers.
8. **walked**   Mrs. Fong **walked** her dog today.
9. **told**   Carlos **told** a funny story.
10. **helped**   Mrs. Garcia **helped** me with math.
11. **called**   I **called** Grandpa on his birthday.
12. **rained**   It **rained** all day on Saturday.

STEP 2 Write Your Spelling List

STEP 3 Set Your Learning Goal

My spelling list has _____ words.

> I always have more than two words to add.

> Each week, our teacher says we should add at least two words from our writing to our spelling lists.

STEP 4 Explore the Spelling Pattern
Sorting Words

You may wish to use **Hands-on Word Sort Cards** and the **Hands-on Word Sort Sheet** for this unit.

Read the **Pattern Words** out loud with a partner. Listen to how **-ed** sounds in each word. Sort the words into four groups. If a word doesn't fit with a word below, put it with the question mark. Write each **Pattern Word** once.

1. looked
(-ed sounds like t)

2. played
(-ed sounds like d)

3. needed
(-ed sounds like -ed)

4. ?
(no -ed)

STEP 5 Focus on Word Study
Changes in Spelling

Long ago, an English word spelled **nied** later changed to **nede**. Today we spell the word as **need**.

Write the **Pattern Word** that came from each group of old spellings.

1. helpan, helpen

2. planta, plante

▼▼▼▼▼▼▼▼▼▼▼▼▼
Spelling Pattern

• Listen to **looked**. The ending is spelled **-ed**.

• Listen to **played**. The ending is spelled **-ed**.

• Listen to **needed**. The ending is spelled **-ed**.

STEP 6 Practice Your Spelling List Independently

Choose at least three activities to practice your spelling list.

Game Mats	With a Partner	On Your Own	At Home
○ Funny Faces ○ Ski Race	○ Spelling Tic-Tac-Toe	○ Flip Folder ○ Spelling Study Strategy	○ Take Your List Home

Practice the Spelling Pattern

Unscramble each **Pattern Word**. Write the **Pattern Word** and circle **ed**. You'll use eight **Pattern Words**.

Pattern Words

looked
played
needed
bent
wanted
asked
planted
walked
told
helped
called
rained

1. (sekad) a question _____

2. (edaypl) the piano _____

3. (allced) on the phone _____

4. (dewakl) to the store _____

5. (nedede) help _____

6. (riaden) on the umbrella _____

7. (pehlde) a sick friend _____

8. (ntedpla) seeds _____

STEP 7 Focus on Writing

A. Proofread the Writing of Others

Jacy used a spelling checker on the computer to proofread this poem. A spelling checker finds misspelled words. It gives real words you may have meant. Help Jacy choose the correct spelling for the four underlined misspelled words. Write each word he really meant.

When it <u>raned</u> today, I <u>wolked</u> in the rain.

I <u>loked</u> at the shiny drops.

I <u>kalled</u> "hi" to the gray sky.

1. raced	2. walked	3. loved	4. cold
raked	worked	locked	called
rained	walled	looked	killed

1. _____

2. _____

3. _____

4. _____

B. Proofread Your Own Writing

The ending **-ed** may not always sound the same, but it is always spelled the same. Look for words with the ending **-ed** in your writing. Add the words you misspelled to **Words I Need to Know How to Spell**.

C. A Writing Idea: A Paragraph

What day was yesterday? Write a list of things you did yesterday.

STEP 8 Check Your Weekly Progress

▶ **Take the Test**

▶ **Check Your Goal**

▶ **Graph Your Progress**

▶ **Save Missed Words**
Write the words you missed in your list of **Words I Need to Know How to Spell**.

SPELLING PATTERN

26

Plurals: -s, -es

Build Your Spelling List

Find Your Pattern Words

Add Teacher Words

Add Your Words

Pattern Words

1. **boats**   The **boats** went down the river.
2. **birds**   Do you hear the **birds** singing?
3. **wishes**   Do your **wishes** come true?
4. **inches**   There are 12 **inches** in a foot.
5. **houses**   I counted all the white **houses** I saw.
6. **dresses**   Kim got two new **dresses**.
7. **boxes**   Please put the books in the **boxes**.
8. **horses**   My grandmother owns three **horses**.

STEP 2 Write Your Spelling List

STEP 3 Set Your Learning Goal

My spelling list has _____ words.

Maybe it's better just to add the words you miss on the pretest.

I add the whole **Pattern Words** list to my spelling list.

STEP 4 Explore the Spelling Pattern
Sorting Words

Sort the **Pattern Words** into two groups. Use the words below to guide your sort. Make sure you write each **Pattern Word** once.

Try sorting the words in other ways. Which words have two syllables?

1. houses (house)

_____
_____
_____
_____
_____
_____
_____

2. wishes (wish)

_____
_____
_____
_____
_____
_____
_____

▼▼▼▼▼▼▼▼▼▼▼▼▼
Spelling Pattern

- Listen to **boats** and **birds**. The plural ending in these words is spelled **-s**.

- Listen to **wishes** and **inches**. The plural ending in these words is spelled **-es**.

· · · · · · · · · · · · · · · · ·

STEP 5 Focus on Word Study
Word History

Do boxes grow on trees? Long ago, people made the first boxes with wood from the box tree. Our word **box** comes from the name of this tree. The word is the same, but the meaning has changed.

1. Choose the word that once meant how long a king's thumb was. (foot, inch)

2. Which word once meant how long the king's shoe was? (foot, inch)

_____
_____
_____
_____

STEP 6 Practice Your Spelling List Independently

Choose at least three activities to practice your spelling list.

Game Mats

○ Ski Race

○ Spelling Road Race

With a Partner

○ Spelling Tic-Tac-Toe

On Your Own

○ Flip Folder

○ Spelling Study Strategy

At Home

○ Take Your List Home

 Practice the Spelling Pattern

Write a **Pattern Word** to complete each "math sentence" below.

Pattern Words

boats
birds
wishes
inches
houses
dresses
boxes
horses

1. 1 bird + 1 bird = 2 __

2. 1 box + 1 box = 2 __

3. 1 dress + 1 dress = 2 __

4. 1 wish + 1 wish = 2 __

5. 1 boat + 1 boat = 2 __

6. 1 horse + 1 horse = 2 __

7. 1 inch + 1 inch = 2 __

8. 1 house + 1 house = 2 __

STEP 7 Focus on Writing

A. Hunt Spelling Words in Your Writing

Choose one piece of your writing. Work with a partner to look for words with the plural endings -s and -es. Use columns like these to write the words you found.

Make a capital.
Make a small letter.
Add something.
Take out something.
Add a period.
New paragraph
SP Spelling error

Column 1	Column 2
I spelled these words with the endings -s and -es correctly.	I misspelled these words with the endings -s and -es.

If you can't find any words with the endings -s and -es, choose a different piece of your writing.

Add the words you wrote for Column 2 to **Words I Need to Know How to Spell**.

B. A Writing Idea: A Comparison

Work with a partner to make a list of words that tell about boats. Make another list of words about birds. Write a few sentences that tell how birds and boats are alike and how they are different.

STEP 8 Check Your Weekly Progress

▶ **Take the Test**

▶ **Check Your Goal**

▶ **Graph Your Progress**

▶ **Save Missed Words**
Write the words you missed in your list of **Words I Need to Know How to Spell.**

SPELLING STRATEGY

27

Write and Check

STEP 1 **Build Your Spelling List**

Find Your Strategy Words

Add Teacher Words

Add Your Words

Strategy Words

1. **said** Dad **said** I may go with you.
2. **goes** Our class **goes** to the school library every Friday.
3. **walk** I'll take the puppy for a **walk**.
4. **now** Anthony has to go home **now**.
5. **know** I **know** all my spelling words.
6. **going** Are you **going** to the party?
7. **has** Susan **has** a new kitten.
8. **dear** They loved their **dear** grandmother.

STEP 2 **Write Your Spelling List**

STEP 3 **Set Your Learning Goal**

My spelling list has _____ words.

> Our teacher writes words to add to our spelling lists on the chalkboard.

> When I copy them, that part of my list is already done.

132   **UNIT 27**

Explore the Spelling Strategy
Which Letters Match?

Write a **Strategy Word** to finish each sentence. (Hint: The underlined letters are clues to the **Strategy Word**.)

1. The baby is learning to __ and t<u>alk</u>.

2. The c<u>ow</u> wants to eat right __.

3. A __ little bunny hopped n<u>ear</u> me.

4. A sock __ over your t<u>oes</u>.

5. Do you __ how to tie a <u>kn</u>ot?

6. He __ lost <u>hi</u>s hat.

7. Are we __ to go soon?

8. I __ you could help s<u>ai</u>l the boat.

1. _____

2. _____

3. _____

4. _____

5. _____

6. _____

7. _____

8. _____

Focus on Word Study
Related Words

Walk means to go somewhere on foot. But **walk** is also used with other words to form related words with new meanings. A **walking stick** is a stick someone uses when walking.

Write **walkout, walkie-talkie,** or **walkway** to complete each sentence.

▼▼▼▼▼▼▼▼▼▼▼▼▼▼▼

Spelling Strategy
If you're not sure how to spell a word, write it out. Check to see if your spelling is correct.

■ ■ ■ ■ ■ ■ ■ ■ ■ ■ ■ ■ ■ ■

1. A path for walking is a __.

2. During a __, people leave suddenly as a way of protesting.

3. You can use a __ to talk with someone in a different place.

STEP 6 Practice Your Spelling List Independently

Choose at least three activities to practice your spelling list.

Game Mats	With a Partner	On Your Own	At Home

- ○ Spelling Road Race
- ○ Spelling Snakes
- ○ Spelling Tic-Tac-Toe
- ○ Flip Folder
- ○ Spelling Study Strategy
- ○ Take Your List Home

 Practice the Spelling Strategy

One **Strategy Word** in each sentence is written three different ways. Write the correct spelling.

Strategy Words

said
goes
walk
now
know
going
has
dear

1. My bike (has, hass, haz) a red horn. _____

2. She said, "Oh (dear, dere, daer)!" _____

3. We can (wawk, wak, walk) to the park. _____

4. It's time to go to bed (noww, nou, now). _____

5. He (goes, goz, gose) to the farm every year. _____

6. I don't (now, know, no) where my hat is. _____

7. Where are you (gowing, goong, going)? _____

8. She (sed, said, sead), "Open your books." _____

STEP 7 Focus on Writing

A. Proofread the Writing of Others

Proofread this paragraph. Decide which type of mistake, if any, appears in each underlined part.

I'm <u>goeing to a museum</u>. This museum
①
<u>haz lots</u> of dinosaur bones. <u>some dinosaurs</u>
② ③
were very big. Some <u>people now think the</u>
④
skin of dinosaurs was colorful.

Make a capital.
Make a small letter.
Add something.
Take out something.
Add a period.
New paragraph
Spelling error

1. **A** Spelling
   B Capitalization
   C Punctuation
   D No mistake

2. **A** Spelling
   B Capitalization
   C Punctuation
   D No mistake

3. **A** Spelling
   B Capitalization
   C Punctuation
   D No mistake

4. **A** Spelling
   B Capitalization
   C Punctuation
   D No mistake

B. Proofread Your Own Writing

Look for **Strategy Words** in your writing. Check to be sure you have spelled them correctly. Write misspelled words in **Words I Need to Know How to Spell**.

C. A Writing Idea: A Friendly Letter

Make a list of ideas you want to put in a letter to someone. Use the list to write your letter.

STEP 8 Check Your Weekly Progress

▶ **Take the Test**

▶ **Check Your Goal**

▶ **Graph Your Progress**

▶ **Save Missed Words**
Write the words you missed in your list of **Words I Need to Know How to Spell**.

SPELLING PATTERN

28

Final Consonants: ll, ss

STEP 1

Build Your Spelling List

Find Your Pattern Words

Add Teacher Words

Add Your Words

Pattern Words

1. **tall** — Are you as **tall** as I am?
2. **kiss** — Dad always gives me a **kiss** goodnight.
3. **fill** — Please **fill** this can with red paint.
4. **moss** — There is **moss** growing on this tree.
5. **full** — This box is **full** of old toys.
6. **still** — Are you **still** playing that game?
7. **wall** — We have one more **wall** to paint.
8. **pull** — I'll **pull** you in the wagon.

STEP 2

Write Your Spelling List

STEP 3

Set Your Learning Goal

My spelling list has _____ words.

If I see some really cool words, I add them to my spelling list.

Me, too! Those words make my writing more fun to read.

STEP 4 Explore the Spelling Pattern
Sorting Words

Sort the **Pattern Words** into two groups. Use the underlined parts of the words below to guide your sort. Write each **Pattern Word** once.

> Try sorting the words in other ways. Write the words in A-B-C order.

1. ta<u>ll</u>

2. ki<u>ss</u>

STEP 5 Focus on Word Study
Spelling in Different Languages

A kiss on the cheek shows love in many countries. The words for **kiss** sometimes look and sound alike in other languages, too. For example, in Sweden, the word is **kyssa**. In Denmark, it is **kysse**. And in Germany, it is **küssen**.

1. Which **Pattern Word** do you think is spelled **still** in German and **stil** in Dutch?

2. Write the **Pattern Word** that the French call **mousse** and the Germans call **Moos**.

▼▼▼▼▼▼▼▼▼▼▼▼▼▼
Spelling Pattern

- Listen to **tall**. The last sound in the word **tall** is spelled **ll**.

- Listen to **kiss**. The last sound in the word **kiss** is spelled **ss**.

UNIT 28 **137**

STEP 6 Practice Your Spelling List Independently

Choose at least three activities to practice your spelling list.

Game Mats

○ Spelling Snakes   ○ Funny Faces

With a Partner

○ Spelling Tic-Tac-Toe

On Your Own

○ Flip Folder   ○ Spelling Study Strategy

At Home

○ Take Your List Home

Practice the Spelling Pattern

Use a **Pattern Word** to complete each rhyme.

Pattern Words

tall
kiss
fill
moss
full
still
wall
pull

1. Mama says that she will miss me.
   She can't wait to hug and __ me.

   _____

2. My big brother's not short at all.
   He seems like he's ten feet __.

   _____

3. I made this picture of the trees in fall.
   See—I hung it on my __.

   _____

4. In the forest, you may walk across
   some green, brown, or golden __.

   _____

5. I just talked to my brother, Bill.
   He says it's too cold to swim—__!

   _____

6. John can't pull the wagon for us,
   because it is too __ of us!

   _____

7. The sun will make my painting fade.
   Would you please __ down the shade?

   _____

8. A little more, but please don't __ it.
   If it's too full, I might spill it!

   _____

STEP 7 Focus on Writing

A. Proofread the Writing of Others

Check Tia's paragraph for spelling errors. Find the four words that are not spelled right. Write the correct spelling of each word.

The old stone wall near my house is not tal. Moz grows on it. The dirt near the wall is foll of ant hills. I wonder what the ants fil their hills with!

Make a capital.
Make a small letter.
Add something.
Take out something.
Add a period.
New paragraph
SP Spelling error

1. _____

2. _____

3. _____

4. _____

B. Proofread Your Own Writing

The last sound in **tall** is spelled **ll**. The last sound in **kiss** is spelled **ss**. Look in your writing for words that end with these sounds. Add any misspelled words to **Words I Need to Know How to Spell**.

C. A Writing Idea: A Description

Look around your classroom. Make two lists. Use columns like these to write your lists.

| Things on the Walls at School | Things on the Walls at Home |

Choose one thing. Write a description of it.

STEP 8 Check Your Weekly Progress

▶ **Take the Test**

▶ **Check Your Goal**

▶ **Graph Your Progress**

▶ **Save Missed Words**
Write the words you missed in your list of **Words I Need to Know How to Spell**.

SPELLING PATTERN

29

Endings: -ed

STEP 1 Build Your Spelling List

Find Your Pattern Words

Add Teacher Words

Add Your Words

Pattern Words

1.	**started**	The concert **started** late.
2.	**hoped**	Dana **hoped** for good weather today.
3.	**hopped**	The rabbit **hopped** into the bushes.
4.	**liked**	Nelda **liked** the necklace I made.
5.	**loved**	I **loved** the movie we saw last night.
6.	**named**	Have you **named** your puppy?
7.	**saved**	We **saved** our cans for recycling.
8.	**patted**	I **patted** the puppy's head lightly.
9.	**tapped**	Mom **tapped** Jill on the shoulder.
10.	**hummed**	We **hummed** the song.
11.	**hugged**	My brother **hugged** his stuffed bear.
12.	**stayed**	We **stayed** at school to wait for Dad.

STEP 2 Write Your Spelling List

STEP 3 Set Your Learning Goal

My spelling list has _____ words.

I seem to be word hunting all the time.

Me, too! Hunting words is easy. And it's fun!

STEP **4**

Explore the Spelling Pattern
Sorting Words

Find a partner. Read the **Pattern Words** out loud. Think about how **-ed** changes the spelling of each base word. Sort the **Pattern Words** into three groups. Use the words below to guide your sort. Write each **Pattern Word** once.

You may wish to use **Hands-on Word Sort Cards** and the **Hands-on Word Sort Sheet** for this unit.

1. hop<u>ed</u> (hope)	2. hop<u>ped</u> (hop)	3. start<u>ed</u> (start)

▼▼▼▼▼▼▼▼▼▼▼▼▼▼
Spelling Pattern

- When you add **-ed** to a word that ends in **silent e,** drop the **e** and add **-ed**: **hope, hoped**.

- When you add **-ed** to a word that ends with one vowel and one consonant, double the consonant and add **-ed**: **hop, hopped**.

STEP **5**

Focus on Word Study
Word History

The base words of **hoped** and **hopped** come from old words that had the meanings below.

Write **hope** or **hop** to fit each old meaning.

1. to bend forward

2. to look for

STEP 6 Practice Your Spelling List Independently

Choose at least three activities to practice your spelling list.

Game Mats

○ Funny Faces ○ Ski Race

With a Partner

○ Spelling Tic-Tac-Toe

On Your Own

○ Flip Folder ○ Spelling Study Strategy

At Home

○ Take Your List Home

Practice the Spelling Pattern

Use each "math sentence" to spell a **Pattern Word**. Write the word. You'll use eight **Pattern Words**.

Pattern Words

started
hoped
hopped
liked
loved
named
saved
patted
tapped
hummed
hugged
stayed

1. hug + g + ed = __

2. love - e + ed = __

3. stay + ed = __

4. pat + t + ed = __

5. hop + p + ed = __

6. save - e + ed = __

7. start + ed = __

8. hope - e + ed = __

Focus on Writing

A. Hunt Spelling Words in Your Writing

Choose one piece of your writing. Work with a partner to look for words with the ending -**ed**. Use columns like these to write the words you find.

Make a capital.
Make a small letter.
Add something.
Take out something.
Add a period.
New paragraph
(SP) Spelling error

Column 1	Column 2
I spelled these words with the ending -**ed** correctly.	I misspelled these words with the ending -**ed**.

If you can't find any words with the ending -**ed,** choose a different piece of your writing.

Add the words you wrote for Column 2 to **Words I Need to Know How to Spell**.

B. A Writing Idea: A Book Report

What book have you read lately that you really liked? Write the name of the book. Make a list of the people or animals in the story. Write a paragraph telling about the book. Give reasons why you think someone else should read it.

STEP 8

Check Your Weekly Progress

▶ **Take the Test**

▶ **Check Your Goal**

▶ **Graph Your Progress**

▶ **Save Missed Words**
Write the words you missed in your list of **Words I Need to Know How to Spell**.

SPELLING PATTERN

30

Endings: -ing

Build Your Spelling List

Find Your Pattern Words

Add Teacher Words

Add Your Words

Pattern Words

1. **eating**   We'll be **eating** dinner at six o'clock.
2. **hoping**   Juan is **hoping** for a sunny day.
3. **hopping**   We saw rabbits **hopping** in the park.
4. **waving**   The flag is **waving** in the wind.
5. **giving**   The teacher is **giving** a test.
6. **making**   Uncle Jim is **making** our lunch.
7. **coming**   Aunt Jo is **coming** on the bus.
8. **putting**   I am **putting** my toys away now.
9. **doing**   What are you **doing** on Saturday?
10. **sitting** We were **sitting** on the floor.
11. **riding**   I was **riding** my bike on the path.
12. **running** Are you **running** in the race?

STEP 2 Write Your Spelling List

STEP 3 Set Your Learning Goal

My spelling list has _____ words.

> And word sorts are really fun with **Hands-on Word Sort Cards!**

> When I sort words, I see how the spelling is the same in different words.

STEP 4 Explore the Spelling Pattern
Sorting Words

Sort the **Pattern Words** by how **-ing** changes the spelling of each base word. Use the words below to guide you. Write each word once.

You may wish to use **Hands-on Word Sort Cards** and the **Hands-on Word Sort Sheet** for this unit.

1. hop<u>ping</u> (hop)

3. eat<u>ing</u> (eat)

2. hop<u>ing</u> (hope)

▼▼▼▼▼▼▼▼▼▼▼▼▼▼

Spelling Pattern

- When you add **-ing** to a word that ends in **silent e,** drop the **e** and add **-ing**: **hope, hoping**.

- When you add **-ing** to a word that ends with one vowel and one consonant, double the consonant and add **-ing**: **hop, hopping**.

STEP 5 Focus on Word Study
More Than One Meaning

Many words have more than one meaning. If you **give** your dad a present you hand it to him. If you **give up,** you've stopped trying.

Write the **Pattern Word** that fits in both places in each sentence.

1. The flag is __ in the wind, and the girl is __ to her friend.

2. The boy is __ in a race, and the water is __ in the sink.

STEP 6 Practice Your Spelling List Independently

Choose at least three activities to practice your spelling list.

Game Mats

 ○ Ski Race

 ○ Spelling Road Race

With a Partner

 ○ Spelling Tic-Tac-Toe

On Your Own

 ○ Flip Folder

 ○ Spelling Study Strategy

At Home

 ○ Take Your List Home

Practice the Spelling Pattern

Write the **Pattern Word** that completes each sentence. The underlined base word is a clue. You'll use eight **Pattern Words**.

Pattern Words

eating
hoping
hopping
waving
giving
making
coming
putting
doing
sitting
riding
running

1. Come and <u>sit</u> by me.
   I'm __ in a tree.

2. Come <u>ride</u> with us.
   We're __ on the bus.

3. Did Sara <u>wave</u> at you?
   Mike is __, too.

4. I can <u>hop</u> like a frog.
   I'm __ on a log.

5. Do you like to <u>run</u>?
   I like __ in the sun.

6. Tao will <u>come</u> today.
   Hoy is __ Monday.

7. What will you <u>give</u> Joy?
   I'm __ her a toy.

8. Can you <u>make</u> a pie?
   I'm __ one for Guy.

STEP 7 Focus on Writing

A. Proofread the Writing of Others

Proofread Mary's news story. Write the correct spelling of the four underlined **Pattern Words**.

Make a capital.
Make a small letter.
Add something.
Take out something.
Add a period.
New paragraph
SP Spelling error

People were having fun at the Town Fair. Happy children were <u>hoping</u>[1] up and down. People were <u>dueing</u>[2] many different things. Some were <u>rideing</u>[3] on the rides. Some were <u>eatting</u>[4] picnic lunches.

1. _____   3. _____

2. _____   4. _____

B. Proofread Your Own Writing

When you add **-ing** to a word, you may need to drop a **silent e** or double a final consonant. Look in your writing for words with the ending **-ing**. Write any misspelled words in **Words I Need to Know How to Spell**.

C. A Writing Idea: A Personal Story

What do you like to do on Saturday? Write a list. Choose one thing and write a paragraph or two about it. Tell where you were, what you did, and who was with you.

STEP 8 Check Your Weekly Progress

▶ Take the Test

▶ Check Your Goal

▶ Graph Your Progress

▶ Save Missed Words
Write the words you missed in your list of **Words I Need to Know How to Spell**.

UNIT 30   **147**

SPELLING PATTERN

31

Compound Words

STEP 1 Build Your Spelling List

Find Your Pattern Words

Add Teacher Words

Add Your Words

Pattern Words

1. **doghouse**   The dog is in the **doghouse**.
2. **inside**   Please go **inside** before it rains.
3. **raincoat**   My yellow **raincoat** kept me dry.
4. **outside**   We went **outside** after lunch.
5. **baseball**   Mario threw the **baseball** to me.
6. **bluebird**   Grandpa said a **bluebird** built a nest in that tree.
7. **playpen**   Dad put the baby in the **playpen**.
8. **sailboat**   We saw a **sailboat** on the lake.

STEP 2 Write Your Spelling List

STEP 3 Set Your Learning Goal

My spelling list has _____ words.

I can use activities and game mats to practice *any* words.

Right! **Spelling Road Race** works every time with any spelling list.

STEP 4 Explore the Spelling Pattern
Two Together Make One!

Some words are made up of two smaller words. Use the "math sentences" below to make compound **Pattern Words**. Write the words.

1. out + side = __

2. in + side = __

3. blue + bird = __

4. sail + boat = __

5. base + ball = __

6. play + pen = __

7. dog + house = __

8. rain + coat = __

1. _____

2. _____

3. _____

4. _____

5. _____

6. _____

7. _____

8. _____

STEP 5 Focus on Word Study
Idioms

Have you ever heard someone say that a person is "in the doghouse"? People say this about someone who is in trouble. The person is not really in a house made for a dog. It's just a saying.

Choose a compound word to complete each saying.

1. follow in someone's __ (footsteps, toenails)

   _____

2. make a __ for (butterfly, beeline)

   _____

Spelling Pattern
Listen to **doghouse**. **Dog** and **house** make **doghouse**. **Doghouse** is a compound word because it is made by putting two words together.

STEP 6 Practice Your Spelling List Independently

Choose at least three activities to practice your spelling list.

Game Mats

○ Spelling Road Race   ○ Spelling Snakes

With a Partner

○ Spelling Tic-Tac-Toe

On Your Own

○ Flip Folder   ○ Spelling Study Strategy

At Home

○ Take Your List Home

Practice the Spelling Pattern

In each sentence, find the two words that make a compound **Pattern Word**. (They might not be in the right order!) Write the **Pattern Word**.

Pattern Words

doghouse
inside
raincoat
outside
baseball
bluebird
playpen
sailboat

1. She hit the ball and ran to first base.

2. Our dog has a house in the yard.

3. That pen is a safe place for the baby to play.

4. He put on his coat and walked in the rain.

5. I went out the door on the side of the shop.

6. My brother will sail the boat down the river.

7. The bird has bright blue feathers.

8. What's in the hole by the side of the road?

Focus on Writing

A. Proofread the Writing of Others

Roberto asked a classmate some questions.
Proofread the questions and answers that Roberto
wrote. Find the four words that are not spelled
right. Write the correct spelling of each word.

Q. What things do you like to do outsid?
A. I like to play bazeball and ride in a
    saleboat.

Q. Do you have any pets?
A. I have a dog named Doc. He sleeps in
    a doghowse.

1. _____   3. _____

2. _____   4. _____

B. Proofread Your Own Writing

Look for compound words in your latest piece
of writing. Check to be sure you spelled them
right. Write any misspelled compound words
in **Words I Need to Know How to Spell**.

C. A Writing Idea: A Description

Draw a picture of a dog. Then write a paragraph
to describe the dog. Tell about its size, shape,
and color. Ask a partner to read what you wrote
and to draw that dog. Compare your drawings.
Do the dogs look alike?

 **Check Your Weekly Progress**

▶ **Take the Test**

▶ **Check Your Goal**

▶ **Graph Your Progress**

▶ **Save Missed Words**
Write the words you
missed in your list of
**Words I Need to
Know How to Spell**.

SPELLING PATTERN

32

Homophones

STEP 1 Build Your Spelling List

Find Your Pattern Words

Add Teacher Words

Add Your Words

Pattern Words

1. **hear**   Can you **hear** the music?
2. **here**   Suki asked us to meet her **here**.
3. **hour**   The show starts in one **hour**.
4. **our**   **Our** team won the game.
5. **are**   These apples **are** for your family.
6. **to**   We'll go **to** the store after school.
7. **too**   We had **too** many people for one team.
8. **two**   My sister is **two** years old.

STEP 2 Write Your Spelling List

STEP 3 Set Your Learning Goal

My spelling list has _____ words.

The spelling test shows me how I'm doing every week.

I like **Check Your Progress**! It helps me check how well I remember the spelling patterns.

STEP 4 Explore the Spelling Pattern

Match-up

Some words sound alike but have different meanings. Write the **Pattern Word** that matches each meaning.

1. belongs to us
2. part of a day
3. he is, she is, they __
4. in this place
5. listen to
6. next after "one"
7. toward
8. more than enough

1. _____

2. _____

3. _____

4. _____

5. _____

6. _____

7. _____

8. _____

STEP 5 Focus on Word Study

Changes in Meaning

How many minutes are in one hour? The word **hour** comes from a very old word that meant "season." Much later, **hour** came to mean "sixty minutes."

1. Write the **Pattern Word** that used to mean "this one." (hear, here)

   _____

2. Which **Pattern Word** once meant "to notice"? (hear, here)

   _____

Spelling Pattern

Words that sound alike but are spelled differently are called **homophones**. You need to know the spelling that goes with the meaning you want.

STEP 6 Practice Your Spelling List Independently

Choose at least three activities to practice your spelling list.

Game Mats	With a Partner	On Your Own	At Home

- ○ Funny Faces
- ○ Spelling Snakes
- ○ Spelling Tic-Tac-Toe
- ○ Flip Folder
- ○ Spelling Study Strategy
- ○ Take Your List Home

Practice the Spelling Pattern

Choose the correct homophone to finish each sentence.

Pattern Words

hear
here
hour
our
are
to
too
two

1. Happy birthday __ you!
   (to, too, two)
   _____

2. There are __ shoes in a pair.
   (to, too, two)
   _____

3. My brother is __ little for school.
   (to, too, two)
   _____

4. This is __ house.
   (are, hour, our)
   _____

5. Tony and Shane __ on the bus.
   (are, hour, our)
   _____

6. One __ is the same as 60 minutes.
   (are, hour, our)
   _____

7. Can you __ the music?
   (hear, here)
   _____

8. We can play ball __.
   (hear, here)
   _____

STEP 7 Focus on Writing

A. Proofread the Writing of Others

Proofread this paragraph. Decide which type of mistake, if any, appears in each underlined part.

Mrs. Perez came to <u>are class</u>. She is from
①
Mexico. She <u>showed</u> us a <u>film</u> about Mexico.

<u>then she sang</u> songs. It was <u>fun to here her</u>
②   ③
sing in Spanish. She stayed <u>about one hour</u>
④

1. **A** Spelling
   B Capitalization
   C Punctuation
   D No mistake

2. **A** Spelling
   B Capitalization
   C Punctuation
   D No mistake

3. **A** Spelling
   B Capitalization
   C Punctuation
   D No mistake

4. **A** Spelling
   B Capitalization
   C Punctuation
   D No mistake

B. Proofread Your Own Writing

Writers often misspell words that sound alike. Look for homophones in your writing. Make sure you spelled them correctly.

C. A Writing Idea: A Song

List things you can count by twos, such as boots, socks, ears, or eyes. Use your list to write a song. Sing your song to music you know.

STEP 8 Check Your Weekly Progress

▶ **Take the Test**

▶ **Check Your Goal**

▶ **Graph Your Progress**

▶ **Save Missed Words**
Write the words you missed in your list of **Words I Need to Know How to Spell**.

Check Your

✓ Check Your Spelling

Review Test

Here is a fun way to review your progress on spelling patterns. First, take the review test your teacher will give you. Then, check your test.

1 _____

2 _____

3 _____

4 _____

5 _____

6 _____

7 _____

8 _____

9 _____

10 _____

11 _____

12 _____

Progress

Which words did you spell correctly? Use the **Spelling Pattern Mastery Chart** to find your mastery level for each spelling pattern.

Spelling Pattern Mastery Chart

Pattern	All Correct	None Correct
Endings: -ed 5		
Plurals: -s, -es 7	11	
Final Consonants: ll, ss 1	9	
Endings: -ed 2	4	
Endings: -ing 6	10	
Compound Words 12		
Homophones 3	8	

All Correct: Pattern Mastered
None Correct: Keep Working on the Pattern

✓ Check Your Writing

Work with a partner to check your writing for words that match each pattern. Write misspelled words in your **Words I Need to Know How to Spell**.

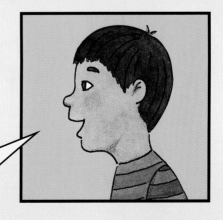

Spelling and Handwriting

Good handwriting makes it easier for others to understand your good ideas.

Letter	Common Problems	Incorrect letter form makes word appear misspelled	Correct
o	*o* OPEN	doll	doll
n	*r* LETTER IS NOT COMPLETE	row	now
e	*c* NO SLIDE RIGHT STROKE	car	ear
a	*a* OPEN	far	far

Manuscript Alphabet

MORE WORDS FOR
Hungry WORD Hunters

When you build your spelling list each week, you might choose from these lists. These words match the pattern or strategy in each unit.

Unit 1

Spelling Is Important

am
at
can
hat
him
in
it
yes

band
felt
lift
nest
rich
swam
tent
test

Other Strategy Words

big
cot
flap
ham
ink
mug
nap
rent
silk
sung

Math Strategy Words

dollar
puzzle

Science Strategy Words

fawn
giant
spider

Social Studies Strategy Words

hoe
winner

Unit 2

Short Vowels: a, e, i

dad
did
man
pet
sat
sit
six
ten

belt
camp
drink
less
list
pass
spend
win

Other Pattern Words

as   fit
bell   pill
bill   press
desk   ring
fat   sad

Math Pattern Words

fifty
gram
penny
sixty
tens

Science Pattern Words

melt
piglet
web

Social Studies Pattern Words

apple
ax
dentist

Unit 3

Short Vowels: o, u

box
but
mom
pop
run
sun
up
us

lock
odd
pond
shot
such
thumb
uncle
under

Other Pattern Words

clock
drum
dust
flock
hunt
mud
nod
pocket
rub
smock

Math Pattern Words

number
sum

Science Pattern Words

bulb
gums
lungs
mumps
scrub

Unit 4

Use Rhyming Words

bake
bug
car
day
hug
pan
rug
sat

bark
blow
cream
flow
flower
lamp
sound
throw

Other Strategy Words

blink
chalk
frown
stood
swing

Math Strategy Words

half
hour

Science Strategy Words

gas
germ
jaw
roar
sank

Social Studies Strategy Words

hung
rang
tool

Unit 5

Short a: a
Long a: a-C-e

aunt
cage
cap
cape
crash
laugh
place
plan
plane
race
space
state

Other Pattern Words

cane
frame
graze
mask
sack
sand
skate
stamp
tape
wave

Social Studies Pattern Words

grape
parade
race

Unit 6

Long a

able
afraid
bay
brave
flame
gray
mail
main
paint
ray
spray
wait

Other Pattern Words

daisy
hate
laid
maybe
pail
plate
safe
save
stain
tray

Science Pattern Words

maze
raisin
snail

Social Studies Pattern Words

grain
hay

Unit 7

Short e: e
Long e: ee

bed
bee
get
hen
let
see
seed
yes

asleep
ever
free
kept
sled
sweet
west
wheels

Other Pattern Words

empty
greet
left
lemon
necklace
sheep
sleeping
street
week
welcome

Science Pattern Word

heel

Unit 8

Long e

easy
pea
sea
tea
tree

angry
east
every
leave
real
sixteen
steep
team

Other Pattern Words

beef
cheese
funny
meal
mean
neat
puppy
seek
sneeze
sorry

Math Pattern Words

thirty
twenty

Science Pattern Words

heat
squeak

Social Studies Pattern Words

bean
leader
team
weave
wheat

Unit 9

Using a Dictionary

a
boy
but
cow
may
my
sun
toy

above
almost
along
follow
merry
money
paper
word

Other Strategy Words

bank
better
eleven
grip
head
hurry
orange
stump
tank
twist

Math Strategy Words

coin
minus

Science Strategy Words

bounce
cocoon
dental
lion
meter
swamp
tiger

Social Studies Strategy Words

income
rule
silo

Unit 10

Short i, Long i

dim
dime
knife
pipe
rip
ripe
shine
wide

Other Pattern Words

fire
prize
sink
slide
slim
smile
swim
thing
twine
wing

Math Pattern Words

nickel
side

Science Pattern Word

solid

Social Studies Pattern Words

riddle
stripes

Unit 11

Long i

bright
fight
fry
high
mice
might
spy
tide

Other Pattern Words

cry
dry
knight
lime
nylon
pry
sigh
sight
sly
spice

Math Pattern Word

dime

Science Pattern Word

butterfly

Unit 12

Short o, Long o

close
fond
globe
hobby
prove
rob
robe
rod
rode
shove
stone
stove

Other Pattern Words

October
octopus
olive
opera
oval

Science Pattern Words

bones
lobster
sole

Social Studies Pattern Word

doctor

Unit 13

Long o

go
home
low
no
old
rope
so

also
below
bone
bow
coal
load
mole
only
own
soap
sold
zone

Other Pattern Words

coach
float
foam
goat
golden
know
roast
shone
soak
window

Science Pattern Word

toad

Unit 14

Proofreading

come
his
in
it
like
on
was
you

begin
eight
letter
penny
stopped
trying
where
would

Other Strategy Words

any
every
full
o'clock
poor
secret
should
sugar
were
your

Math Strategy Words

foot
guess

Science Strategy Words

foal
leap
nerves
salt water

Social Studies Strategy Words

hammer
loom
toe

Unit 15

Words Writers Use

an
do
for
if
is
of
out

again
around
even
everyone
family
once
world
year

Other Strategy Words

busy
could
friend
from
move
other
people
says
sure
yourself

Unit 16

s Blends

lip
pin
sip
skip
slip
spin
stop
top

sent
smoke
sort
spent
sport
stick
street
study

Other Pattern Words

scarf
scooter
sleeve
small
sneakers
speech
spelling
stork
stump
swing

Science Pattern Words

skin
snail
spider

Social Studies Pattern Word

sprout

Unit 17

Consonant Blends With l

block
class
cloud
flash
floor
please
slept
slide

Other Pattern Words

cloth
flat
fluffy
glossy
pleat
sly

Science Pattern Words

clam
flower

Social Studies Pattern Word

floss

Unit 18

Consonant Blends With r

brought
cross
draw
dream
friend
grew
price
trip

Other Pattern Words

braid
brook
frame
frisky
front
graze
grease
grumpy

Math Pattern Words

bar graph
group

Science Pattern Words

brain
drank
frost
gram

Unit 19

r-Controlled Vowels: ar, or

art
corner
large
morning
party
short
storm
yard

Other Pattern Words

acorn
arm
card
dark
fork
horn
parka
porch
scarf
torn

Math Pattern Word

before

Science Pattern Word

stars

Social Studies Pattern Words

cord
garden
harm

Unit 20

r With Vowels

beard
bread
children
hundred
thorn
throne
tires
tries

Other Pattern Words

bird
forget
grade
modern
true

Math Pattern Words

bar graph
fourth
third
yard

Science Pattern Words

chirp
crab
germ
nurse

Social Studies Pattern Word

yarn

Unit 21

k Sound: k, ck

book
look
neck
pack
sock

alike
awake
broke
check
luck
oak
o'clock
shook
snake
thick
track
trick

Other Pattern Words

cake
cook
dock
kick
lock
pike
sack
shack
shipwreck

Math Pattern Word

nickel

Science Pattern Word

snack

Social Studies Pattern Word

junk

Unit 22

Consonants: ch, sh

cheek
chin
dish
push
shop
shut

beach
chair
chance
crush
fresh
lunch
shall
should

Other Pattern Words

bench
chase
chat
chatter
chop
shade
shape
sharp
shift
shiny

Science Pattern Words

rash
shin
shrimp

Social Studies Pattern Word

trash

Consonants: th

bath
path
the
then
thin
thing
this
with

another
anything
fourth
nothing
teeth
their
think
weather

Other Pattern Words

birth
cloth
depth
health
moth
panther
thimble
those
thread
tooth

Math Pattern Word

thirty

Science Pattern Words

thaw
throat

Family Names

dad
mama
mom
papa
pop
sis

cousin
daughter
grandfather
grandmother
husband
parents
son
wife

Unit 25

Endings: -ed

ended
found
jumped
listed
painted
picked
pulled
reached
showed
swept
turned
wished

Other Pattern Words

drifted
filled
followed
pressed

Science Pattern Word

romped

Unit 26

Plurals: -s, -es

branches
bushes
cages
classes
dishes
eyes
lips
noises

Other Pattern Words

apples
benches
boys
brushes
eggs
girls
pies
things
trains
trucks

Math Pattern Words

even numbers
ones
tens

Science Pattern Words

bones
lungs
nerves

Social Studies Pattern Word

helpers

Unit 27

Write and Check

and
dog
fun
good
had
her
I
one

always
because
believe
carry
does
never
people
teacher

Math Strategy Words

count
liter
second

Science Strategy Words

heart
moo

Social Studies Strategy Words

litter
match
monkey
prance

Unit 28

Final Consonants: ll, ss

all
ball
mess
will

across
boss
dull
guess
hiss
spill
stall
yell

Other Pattern Words

mall
small
squall
toss

Science Pattern Words

chill
ill

Social Studies Pattern Word

tall tale

Unit 29

Endings: -ed

added
batted
closed
dropped
lined
lived
moved
rowed
stepped
tagged
used
zipped

Other Pattern Words

planned
rubbed
spotted
tripped
wrapped

Unit 30

Endings: -ing

becoming
beginning
changing
driving
flying
getting
having
leaving
stepping
taking
talking
winning

Other Pattern Words

baking
choosing
digging
saving
scrubbing
shopping
skating
sledding
sliding
spinning

Science Pattern Word

prancing

Unit 31

Compound Words

bookbag
boxcar
into
pigpen
seesaw
suntan

afternoon
airplane
birthday
everything
himself
railroad
something
without

Other Pattern Words

anybody
anyone
bathroom
bedroom
herself
nobody
notebook
rainbow
shoelace
someone

Science Pattern Words

butterfly
fingernail
toenail

Social Studies Pattern Word

footsteps

Unit 32

Homophones

be
bee
sea
see

bare
bear
grate
great
pair
pear
right
write

Other Pattern Words

meat
meet
oh
owe
sail
sale
tail
tale
yoke
yolk

Math Pattern Words

add (ad)
one (won)
sum (some)

Science Pattern Word

sun (son)

Social Studies Pattern Word

hay (hey)

Color one box for each word you spelled correctly on your unit test. If you spelled more than 12 words correctly, color the graph all the way to the top. Then, at the top of the column, write the number of words you spelled correctly.

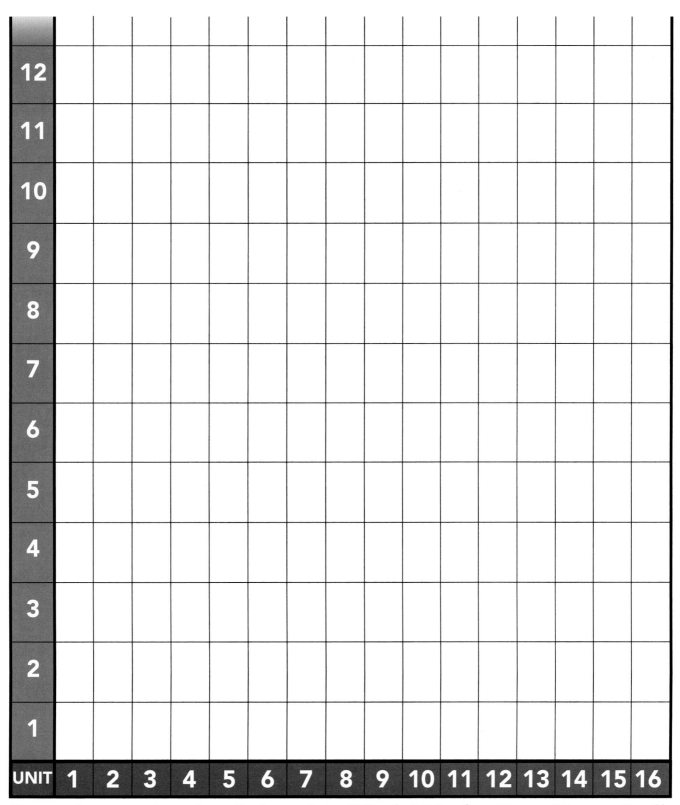

Remember to write misspelled words in **Words I Need to Know How to Spell**.

Graph Your Progress

Color one box for each word you spelled correctly on your unit test. If you spelled more than 12 words correctly, color the graph all the way to the top. Then, at the top of the column, write the number of words you spelled correctly.

Number of words spelled correctly																
12																
11																
10																
9																
8																
7																
6																
5																
4																
3																
2																
1																
UNIT	17	18	19	20	21	22	23	24	25	26	27	28	29	30	31	32

Remember to write misspelled words in **Words I Need to Know How to Spell**.

Words I Need to Know How to Spell

Use **Words I Need to Know How to Spell** to collect words you do not know how to spell. It is the place to write words you have misspelled in your writing or on a unit spelling test. **Words I Need to Know How to Spell** is also a good place to write new words you want to learn to spell.

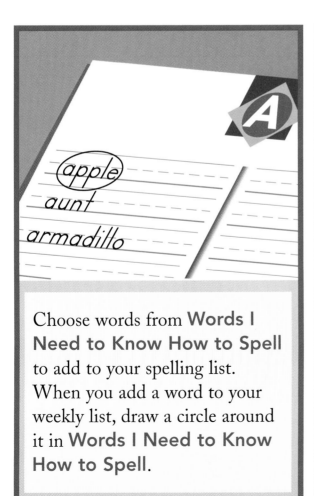

Choose words from **Words I Need to Know How to Spell** to add to your spelling list. When you add a word to your weekly list, draw a circle around it in **Words I Need to Know How to Spell**.

When you spell the word correctly on your unit test, cross it out in **Words I Need to Know How to Spell**. If you misspell the word on your test, add it to another weekly list later. Study the word again.

Strategies for Checking Your Spelling

Strategy: Ask an "expert"

An expert is anyone who is a good speller. It could also be anyone who wants to find out how to spell a word. An expert can be an adult or a classmate. But try not to ask your teacher. If you ask your teacher, you are not doing the thinking, or the hunting, yourself.

Strategy: Check your environment

When you are writing and cannot think of how to spell a word, look around you! The room has many resources that may have the answer you want. A map might be a quick way to check the spelling of a country name. Atlases and globes can help. You can also check encyclopedias, reference books with pictures, travel guides, signs on the walls, word walls, and posters.

When you add words to your **Words I Need to Know How to Spell,** you are building your own spelling dictionary for the words you need when you write.

Strategy: Use a dictionary

Ask your teacher what kind of dictionary is best for you. A picture dictionary might not have all the words you need to write. An adult dictionary might not be the fastest way to find words you need.

How to Use a Dictionary

Guide Words

The **guide words** at the top of each dictionary page can help you find the word you want. The first guide word tells you the first word on that page. The second guide word tells you the last word on that page. Entries on the page are in A-B-C order between these guide words.

A page with these guide words

barn | bell

would contain the words **basket** and **be**. The words **baby** and **can** would not be on this page.

Entries

Words you want to check in the dictionary are called **entries**. Look at the sample entry below:

| entry the correct spelling, broken into syllables | definition   to be sure you have the correct word |

| pronunciation |

pi•an•o (pe **an´**o), a keyboard instrument whose tones come from wires struck by small hammers. *noun, plural* **pianos**

| other spellings   plurals or other word forms are at the end of an entry |

Tips to Find a Word in a Dictionary

- Practice using guide words. Think of words to spell. Use guide words to find each word. Do this until it is easy.

- If you do not know how to spell a word, guess. Try to find the first three letters of the word. (If you just use the first letter, you might take too long.)

- If you can't find a word, think of how else it might be spelled. For example, if a word starts with the **k sound,** the spelling might begin with **k** or **c.**

- Some spellings are listed with the base word. To find **fastest,** you would look up **fast**.

Words I Need to Know How to Spell

Words I Need to Know How to Spell

Words I Need to Know How to Spell